Tales from Turkey

By

Josie Maguire

www.talesfromturkey.com

REDBAK Publishing

i

Tales from Turkey
First edition (paperback)

A REDBAK Publishing Book: ISBN 978-0-9568320-6-1

First published in Great Britain by REDBAK Publishing.

REDBAK Publishing

Printed in Devon UK

Jacket Design by Think Tank Inc Ltd.
Cover Photography by bresserphotos.com
Internal Illustrations by Tym Lawrence

For my true and special love – Chris.

And

For my dearest Turkish family and their families
who have shown me how to 'walk my life' again,
living in this piece of paradise.

Contents

Foreword

I'll fess up right from the start, I am lucky enough to have visited Josie in her idyllic surroundings. I've basked in the sunshine, picked fruit from the trees, tasted the olives and selected fresh figs in the market. I've also experienced the café culture in the nearby Port of Gocek and so I can absolutely see why Josie is so besotted.

You will be envious of me - and certainly Josie - when you read about this part of the world. In *Tales from Turkey* she takes you on a journey from the mountains to the sea and you get a fabulous insight into the wonderful Turkish people and their culture - so very different from Josie's city background.

This is a wonderful 'dipp-in-able' book, humorous short stories that reflect real life in that lush rural idyll. Expect to smile and be entertained but educated too. All of life is here and you will learn how best to deal with everything from wild puppies and chickens, leering 'Romeos' (who later turn out to be married!) making advances in beach cafés, through to having your bikini line waxed, Turkish style - don't do it!

I sure could have made use of her advice on my first visit to the Port, when to the horror of my husband I bought a gorgeous Turkish Carpet at great expense and paid through the nose to have it shipped to the UK. I'm sure Josie could have sorted me out a deal! I love the chapter on cleaning carpets, she says…

'Handmade woven Turkish carpets have been an integral part of Turkish history and culture since before nomadic times. The word kilim *refers to the way a carpet is made.* Kilims *are not just rugs, they have a multitude of uses as tents, luggage, and floor spreads for guests to sit on.'*

It seems she is lucky enough to have hers lovingly hand-washed every few months by the inimitable Selma (if only I had a Selma!) I'm going to imagine mine is a flying carpet and fly there. Hopefully Josie will have a cup of *Çay* waiting.

Janey Lee Grace is the author of number one Amazon bestseller *Imperfectly Natural Woman*. She is the 'Green Queen' and PR Guru of things natural, organic and holistic. She has written several books on health and wellbeing incorporating eco-friendly issues including *Look Great Naturally... Without Ditching the Lipstick*. Janey is also a regular co-host on BBC Radio 2 Steve Wright's afternoon show.

Writer's Note

In writing *Tales from Turkey* I have researched and checked the facts written in this book.

Although they are based on real life, some names, dates and places have been modified for both fictional purposes and to protect sensitivities of neighbours. However, I would like to apologise should any errors remain in terms of general facts about Turkish society and geography, etc.

Come with me on Josie's journey of learning a new way of life.

How it all Began...

Tales from Turkey

For over twenty years I was not a well lady.

Persistently exhausted, I continued living and working long hours. I pushed through all the red lights in a fog. Finally, one evening, I collapsed at work, not for the first time. Realising this was now a serious situation, I telephoned CJ to call my doctor. I found him waiting at my house on arriving home. It was April 1997, six months after CJ and I were married. It turned out to be a devastating illness. I was shocked by the doctor's prognosis. Life changed forever, I was a wilting plant in a pot, looking out at the world, life walking around me, passing me by. I lived in isolation, bewildered by my state of health.

This was not helped by consultants and specialists having no idea what to do with me apart from issuing prescriptions for depression and sleeping tablets and telling me to 'go and have a nice life'.

I went into denial and by 2000 with no improvement I realised I needed to accept my condition before I would recover. I set about managing my own healing and finding a way to create a new life.

One of my complementary practitioners suggested I research southwestern Turkey, the mountains of Portugal or India, which have proven to help people with this condition.

With CJ's help over the next three years I spent a total of fifteen weeks in southwestern Turkey. I lived a quiet life in a house near the healing sea in a natural warm environment. My energy slowly improved as did my feel-good factor. I coped better than I had done in years.

In the summer of 2003, with a big leap of faith, CJ and I boarded a plane to Turkey. The plan was to spend a few months in this healthy coastal environment, and in between, travel back to the UK for treatment to support my health.

Owls follow us wherever we go...

CJ and I have always been followed by Owls. They have become our sign of good luck. We arrived at five in the morning to the sound of them hooting as they perched on a window ledge opposite our new home. The scent of Jasmine filled the air as we walked up the steps to the front door for the first time.

With this good omen we were excited at the prospect of a healthier chapter in both our lives.

The first few months were heady times. As we settled in we felt like half-tourists, half-natives living in a Turkish community. We woke early each morning to the sound of melodious birdsong, pushing open the shutters in our bedroom to the picture postcard view of bright azure skies. We unhurriedly walked to the beach.

I would submerge into the healing sea, energising until I was ready to take on the day.

Back at the house again, I slowly unpacked boxes that arrived by container from the UK via the city of Izmir some three and a half hours away by road.

Workmen came and went to finish work on the house.

A Turkish friend said her neighbour could help me a few times a week around the house. Her name was Cihan (pronounced Gee–Han). She worked tirelessly and was a great support in those early days.

By mid-July, Istanbulians arrived in cars filled with people and packed with provisions. They were to stay for three months. Suddenly our neighbourhood came alive with women shouting from early morning, ordering their husbands and each other. The sound of children laughing filled the air as they played all day in the bright sunshine and shade.

The men played backgammon in between visits to the beach. Each night in the communal area music screeched out from an old battered sound system with flashing disco lights.

One family arrived from around the Black Sea in northern Turkey. The husband was Serjan and his wife Neglin. Their house was set behind ours, totally over the top with garish décor both inside and out. Tall Roman-style pillars graced the double-gated entrance to their garden.

Initially they were friendly and welcoming. They seemed inquisitive about how we were redeveloping our house. Serjan would arrive unannounced to have a look at our new front door or French windows and step into our kitchen uninvited. We thought it was his way of welcoming us and giving his approval into this Turkish community.

Some evenings they invited us to join them for dinner on their terrace. When at the beach, Neglin would appear with her rattan beach mat and sit beside me for a chat in Turkish. All seemed well.

Family and friends came to visit that first summer too, intrigued by our new life, heading home again none the wiser. It did not feel like a relaxing and peaceful time.

In August I returned to the UK as planned, staying until temperatures dropped and I could manage to live in the Turkish heat again.

December came and we bravely spent our first Christmas cold and damp at our house by the sea. Winter brought howling winds, storms and flooding. We fought against the elements with just a traditional fire (a wood-burning soba) to keep us warm. Thankfully, it is a short season.

At the end of the following April, the temperatures rose again. Serjan and Neglin arrived back from the Black Sea armed with a team of workers. Serjan barked orders from early morning until late at night to this poor crew of men. Their house was turned upside down. Hammering, banging and shouting became the order of each day, all done in a haze of thick dust.

We asked politely if it was possible for his workers to start work at 8am and finish at 6pm. Serjan grunted and said yes, but simply carried on doing it his way. I asked Neglin to help me, hoping she would persuade her husband to be more respectful of his new neighbours. He paid no attention to her; he was on a mission to make his house even bigger and better than anyone else's.

We ate dinner on our terrace with dust flowing around us illuminated by headlights, and continuous noise intrusion until eleven at night. Why this manic behaviour we wondered?

I spoke to the manager of the estate; he sympathised and shrugged. 'Serjan is a bit of a bully, so best not to cross him. He had a triple bypass operation last year and his personality has changed since then.'

Nothing was done to help us.

This man continued to play back gammon with Serjan late into each night with glasses of Raki to bolster them.

At my wits end, CJ asked my Turkish doctor, Haluk, to speak with Serjan to explain why I needed quiet hours. Again Serjan said he would honour our wishes, but nothing changed. He simply laughed and pointed his finger at me when he saw me. It was a joke to him.

One night in bed, with little chance of sleep due to the noise and brightness of the floodlights beaming into our bedroom, we got up and went to his house. We pleaded with him to please stop the noise and give us some peace.

He shouted and threatened CJ. Serjan's wife tried to pacify him to no avail. I was appalled and shocked that someone could behave in this aggressive manner. It was the straw that broke the camel's back. We decided it was time to move. We were never going to get through to this barbaric madman who had no respect for anyone, not even his wife. I did not speak to them again. My dream of a simple, healing and peaceful life disintegrated. This was not the Turkey I wished to live or recover in.

I went into a decline health-wise with no energy to manage my days and feeling anxious due to lack of sleep. Were we being naive foreigners thinking we could spend time in Turkey and fit in?

One afternoon, unknown to me, CJ drove to a village where an Englishman named Henry lived, a man he met on a flight a few months before who invited him to his house. On the way, CJ got lost. With directions from a young village boy, he ended up at a boutique hotel called *Cannet* meaning 'paradise'. He spoke to the owner, Ozzie, who booked us in for a long weekend.

The following day we headed for the mountains. Relieved at getting away I could literally hear the silence as I stepped out of our car that first evening. I was surrounded by high mountains, and views that stretched for miles. I felt as if I was back in Biblical times. It took me the whole weekend to wind down and let go of events and the hostility back at our house by the sea.

CJ surprised me by extending our stay by another five days.

In between sleeping, I sat resting on the terraces and gazed at this spectacular calm setting.

Ozzie and I struck up a friendship. Each evening, all three of us sat together eating dinner as the sun set and the moon and stars appeared. These were the magical, quiet surroundings I had hoped to find when we arrived a year before. This was the real Turkey, the one I dreamt about to help me heal and manage my life again.

Ozzie suggested we look at a few houses in the village. They were no more than open four-legged concrete structures. One such building was located below the Hotel.

Still reeling from the incidents at our beach house, I was not interested in viewing properties. However, one morning, I was walking on the rough pathway from the hotel that led down to a narrow country road. It led me back up another track. As I walked along the stony terrain, I was mesmerised by the peaceful scenery. What lay before me was a shell of a would-be-could-be house. There were pale pinkish marble steps leading to a balcony that overlooked a wild and pine tree-laden countryside, untouched for hundreds of years. I looked down the valley asking myself, 'Can I live in such isolation up a mountain away from people and the sea?'

Over the next few mornings I made the same trip back to the concrete structure. Each time I walked to the house, with the warm healing sun on my face, I felt a great oneness in this natural environment. I listened to the birdsong and the sound of the breeze overhead in the tall umbrella-shaped pine trees that surrounded the property. Privacy and space at last, no strange neighbours to deal with.

I had no wish to go back and live near that nasty man and his wife.

So CJ and I spoke to Ozzie who spoke to the people who owned the land. We set about making a plan to redevelop and design the house to meet our needs.

Then it was time for me to return to the UK again for treatment. CJ, bless him, made a promise that if plans went ahead, he would arrange for the house to be completed by my return. It was a challenging task.

How he managed to complete this project I will never know. What I do know is that we were somehow led to this piece of paradise, this healing retreat.

Excited, I returned from Blighty where CJ collected me from the Airport. And so with renewed faith we drove up the mountain to the traditional Turkish village we were about to call home. Another chapter on this Turkish life-path was about to unfold.

Because of the terracotta-coloured outside walls and pinkish marble tiles on the upper balcony, we named our new house, Pink Pines.

And who was there to welcome us on that first night of arrival? Only two cute owls perched on a broken branch of one of the pine trees, who toowit-toowoo'd all night long…

Tales from Turkey

A Helping Hand

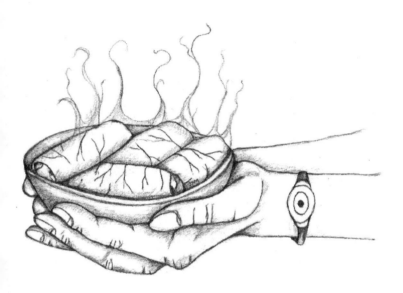

Tales from Turkey

In my dream, a doorbell was ringing. The pitch was so high it startled me out of a deep sleep. Slowly I opened my eyes, looked around the room but nothing seemed familiar. Where am I, and what is that ringing sound? Feeling drugged with sleep and not knowing the time I rolled over and pulled myself up onto the side of the bed. With my brain starting to function, the penny dropped. Late the night before I travelled from the UK where CJ whisked me back to our new home in a Turkish village up a mountain.

I was still two hours behind on UK time. I was grateful that CJ remembered to put my dressing gown on the bed before leaving for work. I put it on and went to open the front door. Standing on the sunny balcony before me was a slip of a girl, as we say in Ireland, looking no more than twenty-one. She had dark-brown eyes, kind and smiling within a round face. She was dressed head-to-toe in shades of blue, yellow and lime green - coordination of colour, there was none.

Every pattern and fabric clashed as if from a psychedelic time machine. Even her headscarf of many colours was trimmed with circles of white lace covering most of her long jet-black hair. Somehow it suited her. She was barefoot.

There was innocence about her as she shyly stepped forward to kiss me on both cheeks.

'Merhaba Joseee, hoşgeldiniz [Hello and welcome]. I am Selma here to help you. Don't worry, I know what to do,' she smiled, wanting to please. 'I have a husband and two children. I cook and keep house. I tend my garden each day.'

I had to trust that she did indeed know what to do, especially on that first morning.

She was armed with a bunch of creamy-white flowering thyme, encased in pink sweet-smelling roses. How kind I thought through my still-foggy brain. She must have been up since the crack of dawn as she also presented me with a pot of steaming hot *dolma* (stuffed vine leaves), and *gozleme* (a cheese and herb-filled pancake).

With only our bed, a kettle, a Turkish teapot, a few tea glasses, some Turkish Tea (*Çay* pronounced 'Chai') from the Black Sea in northern Turkey, and some fresh fruit to keep us going until later that morning, I was all set for a Turkish-type breakfast.

I followed Selma as she headed to the kitchen. Without hesitation this shy young woman cut up some fruit and laid out her food offerings on a plastic fold-up table, complete with two plastic chairs.

Then began the Turkish tea-making.

A day without Turkish tea is like a day without sunshine. The Turkish tea ritual is very much part of the hospitable culture here.

The Turkish teapot consists of one small teapot sitting on top of a larger one.

Selma filled the larger pot with cold water, then placed it on the stove with the small pot on top. Just before the water boiled she removed the small  warmed pot and put several teaspoons of tea in it and replaced its lid. She then placed it onto the large pot. When the large pot boiled, she slowly added the hot water to the dry tea in the small pot until it was half full.

She looked at me and smiled. 'We must let it infuse for five minutes. Then you can eat breakfast.'

While the tea is brewing, let me tell you how Selma came to us. She was recommended by the same hotel owner, Ozzie, who helped to sort out the house details. He knew her family well, and felt we could work together.

In Eastern culture, everything goes through the male head of the house. That said, of course, we women the world over are a force to be reckoned with. We call the shots and make the final decisions in most things, but let the men think otherwise! Even in the East, women are the powers that be, especially in these small villages.

Back in the kitchen, Selma poured the hot liquid nectar into tea glasses until half-full. The taste and flavour of the tea complimented my first breakfast in our place. I ate slowly, savouring each morsel with refreshing sips.

Later that morning Cihan, my housekeeper from our previous house, arrived. She had travelled thirty-five kilometres on the back of an open truck with the contents of our former home. Everything was wrapped in thick blankets and tied up with strong rope. This was the Turkish equivalent of a furniture removal company.

Selma and Cihan introduced themselves to each other, and so began the handover.

They sat cross-legged on the wooden floor in the lounge, exchanging occasional words about their families and backgrounds, unpacking each item carefully.

Then it was time to say a sad goodbye. Tears? Yes, there were many. Loyal Cihan worked with me for nearly two years. I would probably never see her again.

In the months that followed I started to learn Selma's Turkish customs. In particular, the Turkish love of using gallons of water to hose down terraces, and how washing dishes is executed with as many suds and bubbles as possible. Also their love of using far too much washing powder and cleaning products. It makes things cleaner and brighter as seen on the TV, and adverts that never lie! With persuasion and demonstration, thank goodness, only natural products are now used at Pink Pines, with good results.

As for cooking, I have discovered it's better for Selma to peel, chop, grind, blend, grate and prepare some of my food, as opposed to her over-seasoning and cooking the bejasus out of it.

The exception are her soups (çorba, pronounced 'chore-ba') which consists of home-grown vegetables, spices and herbs which are chopped, ground with a large pestle and mortar, and then mixed with yogurt. This mixture is spread onto large metal trays and dried in the hot sun on her terrace until it resembles a powder. Packet soup eat your heart out, this is organic at its best!

CJ enjoys her delicious traditional vegetable dishes too, loaded with garlic, onion, and of course, fresh little red and green chilies, all grown in her garden.

I admire the fact that Selma seems to take everything in her stride. She never moans or throws a strop or gets sulky. She simply says, 'Okey Joseee' to whatever I ask of her (her other English phrase is, 'bye bye'). She has a calm aura as she moves around the house, gliding from room to room. She never rushes and everything is done at an even slow pace. She is not interested in small talk or gossip, which is a blessing to me. Living in such a small village, our position as yabancis (pronounced 'ya-ban-gees' - foreigners to you) is a great source of conversation and amusement to our Turkish neighbours.

As each month passed, Selma blossomed and became more confident. A flurry of excitement at her house was the arrival of a shiny new sewing machine. She made me an enormous rough linen laundry bag tied up with sailor's rope, and twice a week she throws it over her shoulder as she heads downstairs to the laundry room.

She knitted a coffee warmer for the cafetiere, and some cotton and muslin curtains with ties for summer, all hand finished and embellished with beading and shell detail. She is hugely resourceful, no such thing as popping into John Lewis's haberdashery department store to pick up a few trimmings ... oh no, not here.

As she got into her stride, she asked if she could work an extra morning to weed and tidy the garden. Well, what a relief. The terrain is hard, dusty and dry in summer and muddy in winter.

She arrived with a pickaxe and shovel on her shoulder, her skirts tucked into an elastic waistband of what I can only describe as 'pyjama bottoms'. For the next four hours she was on her hands and knees digging, hoeing, weeding and finally planting. No time to stop for a mid-morning coffee and biscuits. She even re-potted and transferred some rather tall prickly cacti to larger pots. Brave lady, I would not have known where to begin, and perish the thought I would scratch or cut my fingers, or even worse, break a nail.

The women in these villages undertake work that we could never imagine doing in the West. They live off the land, planting food in season and bartering with their neighbours who have, honey, livestock and chickens.

Living in this tiny village, I am at the absolute core of a simple, natural life, surviving one day at a time. Fond childhood memories come flooding back of summer holidays in Ireland at my grandmother's house in County Cork.

One morning, Selma's mother-in-law Ebru, who lives further down the track, rounded the hill to our house with Selma following in her footsteps. She bustled into our lounge with a big jolly smile and a large carrier bag under her arm. She was back home after a forty-five day round trip of a lifetime to Mecca. She presented us with a large bag of sweet medjool dates from the Holy City. Then she took out a toy camel. She pressed some buttons and the thing came to life with flashing red eyes, playing a very loud and completely out-of-tune rendition of the Muslim call to prayer.

In the Muslim religion, five times a day, the *Meuzzin* summons the people to pray, reciting these prayers in melodic tones (unlike the flashing camel).

CJ, myself, Selma and Ebru all stood in a circle and laughed until finally the camel was quiet again.

Selma continues to appear with flowers and vegetables, and even cooks food a few times each week, all from her garden, prepared with great love and no expectation of anything in return. I buy bread, fresh fish and sometimes medication for her family when needed as a thank you.

Nearly ten years on I am pleased to report that my Irish way of 'let's simply work together' seems to have good results. What I thought was going to be a domestic jungle as East meets West, merges like Ying and Yang. We continue to adapt to each other, and learn from each other with only the occasional misunderstanding and casualty.

I do lists, and our chats are in Turkish, during which Selma's younger sister sometimes translates. A relationship of acceptance, trust, respect, amusement and huge gratitude has developed between us.

Thankfully, the batteries have since been removed from said flashing red-eyed camel, which remains hidden away until Ebru's next visit.

Tales from Turkey

Be Careful What You Wish For

Wₑ were living in the mountains a few months when CJ mentioned yet again.

'J, wouldn't it be nice to have a dog?'

'Hmmm…' was my guarded response.

Having been bitten by Alsatians as a child - and never owning a dog - I was afraid of these four-legged animals. I agreed to visit the local dog sanctuary in Gocek to take a look. My heart melted on seeing so many dogs in need of a loving family. Even so I left without a new friend.

Two days later out walking along the mountain trail, from nowhere I sensed I was being followed. I looked around and there at my right side was a stocky mongrel the size of a Labrador. There was definitely a mix of goat with a bit of Basil Brush thrown into the tail and foxy face. Her coat was a faded hay colour so she looked like a hairy tub of butter. Her intense dark brown eyes stared up at me as her tail wagged furiously round and round like a propeller. Her body language was asking, 'Please love me, I am very gentle, don't be frightened, I want to be your friend.'

She followed me home, shivering all the way. I telephoned CJ and he suggested I feed her. I found some bits of meat and put them on some foil. She ate the lot, looking for more.

Selma arrived and informed me that the dog's name was Martha and that she appeared one day in the village just a few weeks old. She lived outside most of the time, barking her way through the night and rarely sleeping. Over the years she was passed from one family to another, making her insecure and nervous. Selma believed her to be around nine years old.

Now she was at ours where love, food and security were hers for as long as she wished.

We bought a large dog sofa bed and placed it by the fire. CJ tempted Martha into the house with food and dog biscuits. She took the bait, walked into the lounge, saw the bed and jumped straight in. Cosy and warm she slept all night without a sound.

She never went out again at night unless she had a full moon strop, where days before the full moon her behaviour became erratic and she didn't come in to eat. She ran around the house, then through the forest and down to the mountain road barking at full pitch. CJ would go looking for her many times over the evening with a torch in hand. When she finally appeared all breathless, he calmed her down, put her on a lead and brought her back to the comfort of her bed again.

Each morning she barked her early morning call, 'Come on guys, let's go walking'. As soon as she saw CJ and me putting on our trainers she bounced backwards and forwards, running up and down the marble steps, jumping up on us to get a move-on. Bless her, she seemed to think she was still a puppy and light as a feather. She would happily walk for hours.

On our way back to the house, she loved to drink from the nearby fresh spring and put her paws into the cooling water.

After her exercise she would head off down the dirt track on 'red squirrel watch.' She made the lives of those squirrels hell. She chased them thinking she could catch them, as they ran up a tree. Sometimes she made an attempt to climb the tree, but with her weight there was no chance. Other times she would sit at the base of a telegraph pole, not moving a muscle, staring up at a squirrel perched on top, hoping it was going to come down to meet her wrath. She never learned that they were faster and more agile than her and she was never going to catch one.

She was a popular lady with male dogs as they queued up the track for her attention. She had no problem flirting with 'the boys' and then completely ignoring them if they wished to take things further. Yes, she was 'Martha the tease'.

One such male dog was named Raki after the traditional Turkish drink. He clearly hoped that he and Martha would get it on - not a hells chance. He was half her size with a pale blonde coat. His big sticky-out paws did not match his long and low body. He would appear when he thought we were not around, sip from her water trough and gaze longingly up the stairs to try and catch even a look from the disdainful Martha. He would cock his leg, leaving his scent. Martha pretended he did not exist and would look the other way.

Feeling dejected, Raki would leave the area. But he never gave up and continued to visit, carrying the torch for our dear Martha for over four years.

As for female dogs, well they were given short shrift by Martha if they dared to come onto her patch.

Her healthier eating habits and new exercise regime was making a difference. She looked younger and a happier middle-aged doggie. With all her foibles and comic ways, thanks to Martha I lost my fear of dogs.

CJ's other wish was to have chickens, maybe even a goat or a sheep.

'Let's try and live off the land,' he said, coming over all dreamy and eco-mannish warrior. 'Imagine the joy of collecting eggs each morning and having them fresh for breakfast. Selma could show us how to make our own goat or sheep's yogurt.'

Within weeks of Martha's arrival, lo and behold, a young pale-brown chicken appeared. Martha was not happy about this new-feathered friend's appearance at Pink Pines. Being female and territorial - well she was here first - she growled when Matilda (newly christened by us) came anywhere near her.

Matilda, full of her own importance, would not be put off by a mere dog, and continued to strut her stuff moving amongst the terraces, leaving a runny mess at intervals. We telephoned our neighbours to ask if they were missing a chicken. Back through the airwaves we heard the villagers did not know how this chicken found its way to our house.

A few mornings later, Selma reported that a neighbour, Dilek, living further up the mountain, was indeed missing a brown one fitting the description of Matilda. Obviously, we insisted that Dilek collect Matilda as soon as she could, so she could return to the bosom of her flock. But Dilek generously asked if we would like to keep Matilda as a work-in-progress gift so she could yield us fresh eggs a few months down the line. A daunting prospect for me. Of course CJ the eco-man was as happy as a pig in…

Yet again, his wish was granted.

As for me, well I'm a city girl at heart and consider myself more of a beach babe (well that's how I used to view myself through my rose-tinted glasses). I did not know the first thing about rearing or feeding a chicken, apart from the fact that they lay eggs. Happily, I adapted quickly to Matilda's needs thanks to a little advice from Selma, feeding Matilda every morning and evening with either rice or wheat grains. Yes, her diet is a high carbo, low fat for now. She is thriving.

However, my challenge was finding a way to stop Mattie doing naughties on the sunroof of my car. I discovered that when the sun set she flew onto the roof and curled up and slept until sunrise. Clever girl, but I was not happy that my sunroof was being used in this way. So I spoke with Selma's husband, Ahmet. He promised to build a large nesting chicken coop and run to keep Mattie away from my car, keep her safe at night and give her a warm nesting area to lay her eggs.

Mattie loves a little tickle under the chin. She has a special walk, as if trained in ballet with her very light and precise steps. That said, she can be a noisy little soul. As soon as I appear on the upper terrace she makes a beeline for me with her high-pitched cluck, demanding food. She does not give up easily, being stubborn like her four-legged enemy, dear Martha. She even flies onto my arm and presses her beak into my shoulder in her quest for a few more grains.

CJ is very at ease with Matilda. They have built up quite a rapport as they 'cluck-cluck' to each other every day. I think this is taking being in touch and getting back to nature a little too far.

While CJ's wishes came through, we also found ourselves playing host to other creatures who were not on our wish list.

Various-sized geckos have taken up residence at Pink Pines. There is Little George, who has a swishy turquoise tail. He ambles around us on the lower terrace in the mornings in search of breakfast. When it is hot, he heads to Martha's water, a large log with the centre cut out making two troughs. George jumps onto the top of the log, slides into the water and swims around like a tiny alligator. He then places himself along the top of the trough to sunbathe and dry off. His long tongue flicks in and out as he sips the moisture.

He appears to live in a crevice in the wall on the lower terrace along with other baby geckos that are shy about interacting with us humans. They all seem to keep many of the hairy creepy-crawlies at bay.

Last week I saved a newly-born gecko. It was a dull translucent pink colour with large dark eyes. It was scrambling around the hob on the cooker in the upstairs kitchen. How it got there I will never know. So, brave lady that I am, I deftly put a piece of card under it, followed by a large-brimmed water glass on top. Gingerly, I brought her outside, then removed the water glass and put her gently on the wall of the top terrace. She scrambled up onto the ceiling and still lives to tell her tale.

Another rather plump and salmon-pink female gecko - well she looks female - appears at night on the lower terrace wall. One evening, I also found her in the bedroom dashing in and out from behind pictures. She is a different breed to the others known as an Albino Gecko, but simply known as Pinkie to me.

Another day comes alive. I am off again to hose down the roof of my car and speak with Ahmet to get a wiggle on and build that promised chicken coop.

Selma brought good news from Dilek with her offer of a second chicken as company for Mattie. It's all hands on deck for our new arrival winging its merry way to join Mattie in the next few days.

Oh Brave Women of Turkey
(A Waxing Experience)

I never thought as to how waxing is performed in Turkey. Trying to find a Parlour - I use the word lightly - that will perform a European-style wax, has been a challenging and painfully unforgettable experience.

Believe me, Turkish waxing is not for the faint-hearted. No room for wimps here. I've seen and heard grown women and mothers cry in the name of 'beauty', and so have I.

I have had a few close 'shaves' on more than one occasion.

I discovered that waxing is part and parcel of visiting any hair salon here. They are the hub of all things female: manicures, pedicures, eyebrow plucking, threading and waxing, plus of course anything to do with hair, all take place in these small family-run Parlours. Threading is an art form in itself, and yes, by mistake, I have experienced that pain too.

On my first visit to a Turkish traditional salon, my dear friend Deniz insisted on escorting me. As soon as the word 'wax' was mentioned - quick as a flash - a large pot filled with congealed wax was pulled out and placed in a steel pot on a gas primus stove. When the wax started to bubble, a young girl appeared with a knife and placed it in the pot to sterilize it. I was apprehensive.

Reading my expression, Deniz squeezed my hand. 'J, you are made of strong stuff, you can handle it.'

Like a lamb to the slaughter, I went along with her cajoling and assurances.

The salon was buzzing, a hive of social activity with local women popping in to have their hair cut and coloured whilst they catch up on the local gossip, sipping Turkish tea or coffee.

In Ireland, there are women who have the gift of reading tea leaves. In Turkey women have their coffee cups read, so who needs astrology when your future can be read from the grains of coffee in your upturned decorative china cup? These women knitted and chatted as they happily waited their turn.

Of course I stood out as a yabanci, as I too sat sipping tea waiting patiently. I smiled at the women around me, and they smiled back. The sisterhood united in our efforts to be beautiful and smooth of skin.

Eventually, the owner of the salon, Burcu, appeared and welcomed me. 'Please go behind the curtain, take off your skirt and stand up on the bed in front of you. Hold on to the wall with your back to me.'

A strange request I thought, but did as she asked. Poised and in place for my wax, Burcu appeared wheeling in the pot of molten honey-coloured liquid. She pulled out the knife from the pot and smeared the hot liquid all over my left leg starting at my ankle and working all the way up to my knee. The temperature of the knife on my leg was burning my skin and unbearable.

I yelped like a helpless puppy.

'Can you please cool the knife or the liquid, the wax is burning my skin,' I said through gritted teeth.

She blew on the knife, like that was going to make it cooler. My leg was then completely wrapped in strips of white cotton sheet material. Burcu patted it, and then with an almighty swipe tore the whole of the sheet off my leg.

'Whoa,' I screamed, not caring who heard me. 'Boy, did that hurt.'

I looked over my shoulder and saw what looked like a freshly plucked chicken's leg. My leg was red and raw. Having had one leg done, how could I stop now? I took an extra deep breath and succumbed to the same torture on the right leg. As Burcu tore off the sheeting I screamed out, 'That's it, no more, stop!'

She looked up at me in total surprise, 'What about your bikini line and under your arms?'

I actually had burn marks on both legs by this time. *Get me out of here*, I thought. I just wanted to crawl away, have a coffee with something very strong in it to calm me down. My nerves by this time were shot to pieces.

I pulled on my skirt, pulled back the curtain to pay and escape, where of course I had a full audience, including Deniz, laughing at the poor silly *yabanci*.

She smiled and linked arms with me on my way out. 'What are a few scars in the name of beauty?'

I could have told her in no uncertain terms, but at that moment, feeling quite battered, I just wanted to let my wounds heal and the pain be gone.

Some months later, at a different but highly recommended salon, the owner Zerrin, having finished my leg wax, disappeared only to reappear wielding her hot wax-covered wooden spatula.

'J, are you sure you wouldn't like a Brazilian, it won't take long?'

Are you kidding? With the mental and physical scars of past experiences, never, ever will I consider having a Brazilian, thank you very much. I politely declined.

'So why not try the ball of sugar and honey to do your bikini line?' she suggested. Back she came rolling this ball in her hands. It looked like plasticine.

'Don't worry J, it will be ok,' Zerrin assured me.

Again, I allowed myself to be persuaded. Not a clever move. It felt as if I was skinned alive after she finished.

And still I went back for more punishment. On another visit, Zerrin introduced me to her new assistant, Cihan, who asked if I minded if she did my waxing on that day.

'Only if she can do it the European way,' I replied.

'Oh yes, Cihan knows exactly what to do,' Zerrin assured me again.

Naively, I went behind the canvas and wooden screen. Feeling a little more confident, I hopped onto the bed. Just as I was relaxing, eyes closed, Cihan called out, 'Flex, flex your toes,' as she pushed, pulled and kneaded my skinny legs. I felt every single swipe of the cotton to remove the wax. Perspiration was now rolling off my pinky-red face and arms, and then I felt a clammy fear overtake my body. Cihan had started smearing my bikini line with a lot of wax and then placing long strips of cotton on top. Yep, I took to shouting again, I didn't care who heard. 'Jee…zus, H-Christ, for the love of

God, what are you doing down there?' The sticky wax was stuck to every orifice around that area, even some of it stuck to the cover on the bed I was lying on.

With only half of my bikini done, looking red and raw, no way was I going to let Cihan finish what she had started.

'No', I kept telling her, 'that's it, no more.' I scrambled and fumbled to get dressed with Cihan looking very puzzled at my outburst.

As I pushed back the wooden screen, I shouted across the room at Zerrin, 'Never again Zerrin, do you hear me, never, ever again am I going through this torture.'

My audience sniggered behind their magazines and knitting. Three days later, I was still cutting off bits of wax from odd places and my underwear and bed sheets kept sticking to me. It was not a pretty sight.

Since those heady, searingly painful first experiences, after much research, I found two European-style beauticians, Gul and Nazire, who incur less pain and do a good job to my great relief.

Recently I heard of a yabanci who went into a hair salon in a small town. She allowed the owner to completely thread her legs and bikini line, then wax them 'a la honey and sugar ball'. My source tells me it took nearly three hours. I am squirming and have tears in my eyes at the thought. What was that poor woman thinking and will she ever recover?

My advice (trust me on this), if you are in any way squeamish or have sensitive skin, and you are not living in a bigger town or city, take a major rain check and remember, if you step into a small hair salon in a small town here in Turkey, beware of the scalding pots and knives. If you see them, back pedal, turn right and walk away. You have been warned.

Of course there is always a silver lining, and mine is that through all my experiences of waxing in all the salons I have visited in Turkey, I have never been asked that favourite question, typically said in that squeaky whiney voice used by all hairdressers, beauticians and trainees in UK.

'Going anywhere nice for your holidays?'
We are grateful for small mercies.

Spring is Here
The Grass is Rising…

The days are getting longer and the mornings brighter. The dawn chorus is busy rehearsing their delightful sounds in preparation for the long sunny days ahead. That alone lifts my spirits.

I am surrounded by a landscape that is like an Irish emerald green infinity carpet with large white daisies sweeping across the fields, thanks to the deluge of rain that soaked the land through the short winter months. It feels as if the fairies have been busy painting the mountains and valleys while I sleep. Cornflower blue wild irises and creamy white and yellow roses have sprung into bloom swaying gently in the breeze. Along our mountain roads, large lime-coloured balls of flowers appear at random, contrasting with the bright pink flowers of the oleander bushes. I feel energized, refreshed and ready to take on whatever challenges come my way each day.

We are in the throes of the most beautiful time of the year.

Spring is here.

Our first spring season is called ilk bahar. Then we have a 'second spring' called son baha - or autumn as it is known in the West. Flowers, plants and some vegetables thrive again at this time of year, including our sweet-smelling roses.

This week, our kind neighbour Dilek, as promised, presented us with a playmate and companion for Matilda. So our chicken family is growing. Our new feathered friend is buxom, white with little flecks of grey and is somewhat more ladylike than Mattie who is a bit of a tomboy. So we christened her Beatrice. She was a timid, nervous little soul when she first arrived and our bossy Matilda took advantage of this, especially at feeding time.

Mattie initiated Beatrice on her first morning.

'Just follow me around and do what I do and you'll get in the groove of how things work here. I am not too sure what the lady of the house is feeding me but it is never enough. Just remember that I get first picking to check if it is edible for you, and because I was here first, that's only fair. So no need to rush in. There is a large funny-shaped dog who responds to the name of Martha and she definitely does not like us feathered types, so just ignore her and glide the other way if she approaches.'

After a few days of adjustment these two become joined at the wing, yes, firm friends. They follow each other everywhere, or rather Beatrice struts behind Mattie letting her think that she calls the shots. Mattie kicks up such a fuss when food is around and continues to push Beatrice out of the way at feeding time.

'Beatrice, remember to allow me to test the food first. We don't know what that woman feeds us. You can tell she has never looked after chickens. She has simply no idea.'

To keep me on my toes, Mattie now taps her beak on the window of my office as if to say 'Hurry up, where's my food?' Cheeky bird!

Friends and colleagues have complimented me on my interior design and creative abilities both inside and outside the house and indeed at Pink Pines. Little did I think I would be using these talents to design and help build a chicken shack and run. Selma's husband Ahmet finally appeared to help, and by using recycled bricks and tiles for the shack, and wood and wire for the run, Beatrice and Matilda are now living in the lap of luxury. They appear to be happy in their new environment, the proof of this, having sought advice from other owners, is that they are laying two of the most delicious, deep bright yellow yoked eggs each morning. They are small, perfectly formed and very tasty. Yes, eggs have a great taste once the chickens roam freely and are fed on an organic diet.

We are now accustomed to hearing their early morning laying calls as one protects the other by guarding outside the chicken hutch so they can lay in peace and safety inside. For what seems pure entertainment value, Beatrice and Mattie have perfected a type of line dancing. They do this as part of their scratching ritual in search of food and worms. They have also created a dry dusty bath for themselves in the form of a large hole close to my car, to toss and turn and wave their wings in unison. They sit in this bath for hours on end each day. Unknowingly, we have created a Pink Pines retreat and Zen Spa for chickens and dogs - fully booked for now, I must add!

It is true to say that life is never dull or boring here, hence we have come to expect the unexpected on a daily basis. But around midday on the 29th of March 2005 I was taken by complete surprise, it's a day I shall not forget. An eeriness descended upon the valleys and mountains, something I have not experienced before. A silent darkness that was haunting. Everything stood still and the temperature dropped dramatically. Even though we had blazing sunshine a few minutes before I felt a real chill course through my body. I had goose bumps on my arms and the hairs on the back of my neck stood up. You could have heard a pin drop, literally. I put my knife and fork down on my plate, pushed myself away from the table and sat back in my chair. I took a few deep breaths and relaxed and waited to see and hear what would happen next.

Like a switch being flicked, as if by magic, it suddenly changed to the early hours of the morning. I felt that I had just stepped onto a huge film set, the sky was lit similar to when the full moon lights up the village and valleys. Everything was still. Martha did not feel comfortable and moved into my office to her mat and refused to venture outside. Mattie and Beatrice disappeared into their hutch to sleep. After a while a sole bird started to sing, as if it was sunrise again. Soon this was followed by a gentle and ever-increasing chorus of birdsong. The heat of the day slowly returned with the shadows and spooky atmosphere disappearing. Life then carried on as if nothing had happened. I felt as if I was waking up from a dream.

It was my first experience of a total eclipse.

Some friends had sailed and drove to Kas and Kalkan about two hours east, to see the eclipse. They returned with all kinds of tales.

'You should have been there, it was wondrous. We'll never see anything like that again.'

I was perfectly happy to have experienced it right here sitting on my terrace.

The next eclipse is due in Turkey in fifty years' time. Even with the many elixirs, age-defying technology, miracle creams and positive thinking, I don't think I will be around, unless of course I reappear in another form. Now there's a thought.

With our spring season comes spring cleaning which Selma carries out like a military operation. Out with the old and all that. Everything is washed, scrubbed, vacuumed, cleaned, shaken, brushed, sewn or moth protected. Windows and doors remain open all day, letting in the fresh, clean pine air. Much as we love this reviving fresh air, to our detriment, a 'yellow fairy dust' the colour of pollen appears at night from the pine trees and covers every single centimetre, both in and out of the house, including Martha and my car. Oh boy does my nose and sneezing sessions take their toll on this body at this time of year. We have to accept that it will disappear only when the last of the rain comes to wash and dissolve it all away. Then it's time for Selma to get her brushes, dusters and water hose out again. How the Turkish love hosing things down; it is part of the culture. Thankfully, no water bans here, and just as well.

If I don't get out of the way quickly enough, I am likely to get drenched too. Martha hates the water hose and runs for cover to the office, or heads to the balcony upstairs and hides behind the rattan sofa.

During spring, the women of the village gather leaves from the tops of certain trees. They take them home and boil them *au naturel* (we would lightly steam them) or they cook them with onions and garlic. They are then put in bags and placed in the deep freezer so a natural laxative is always to hand. With these little shoots you need never worry about being constipated again. A few spoonfuls each day and, hey presto, you are sorted forever.

I discovered this brand of laxative by accident last year whilst sampling yet another home-cooked dish from Selma. In fact the villagers do not use these leaves as a laxative, but as an accompaniment to fish, vegetables or *macari*.

'Why do you not eat more of this green food?' Selma asks.

Well, err, how can I tell her without upsetting her?

She adds, 'J, these shoots are filled with goodness, iron and vitamins.'

For me, 'packed with' is usually the Western way of describing any food they wish to market and promote in the name of health. But if Selma says it is so, I'm happy to believe it's true. So who needs three to five spirulina or chlorella tablets a day when I can eat cooked leaves from the top of a tree?

As I write, I can see her picking a few more kilos of these green shoots and placing them into a very large sack.

I know what is on her menu for dinner this evening and maybe even mine. Perhaps I should eat just a little more of this 'miracle food' she raves about? Not only would it keep her happy, but everything moving too.

It's time for lunch methinks, and a chance to yet again soak up the special freshness of my spring surroundings.

Sleepy Sundays
(in Port Gocek)

It's eight in the morning and the sun is just rising over the reddish rock face surrounding us on three sides. CJ and I bump and chug along the track in my little car as we drive down nine kilometres to the main road. Yet again I am blown away by the bright hues of blue and green of our natural landscape.

It's Sunday, which means it's Gocek market day.

As the temperature rises to over thirty-five degrees the normal hustle and bustle in the little Port of Gocek slows, although everyone still moves with purpose.

On Sundays especially there is an attitude of 'no need to hurry'. Nothing happens until 11am and even then things are done with a measure of reluctance. This is not restricted only to the human residents; the local cats and dogs remain curled up, asleep under the shade of the trees or brightly-flowering hibiscus and pink oleander bushes. It's too much effort to yawn, do a yoga stretch or wag a tail, let alone move around.

Walking into the market, there are already groups of stallholders with their families setting up their produce in anticipation of the long hot day.

We head to buy fruit and vegetables before 9am, as it is relatively cool then and the produce is still looking vibrant and fresh. At this time of year, the market is awash with colourful seasonal fruits: fresh cherries, strawberries, apricots and peaches. The giant green and yellow-striped water melons are cut open to reveal their mouthwatering crimson flesh. They sit amongst fresh crisp lettuces, large-leaved peppery rocket and small aromatic sweet tomatoes from the vine. The smell and atmosphere is intoxicating. What a way to start our day.

One fruit I came to taste since living here is the musmala. The Turks also call it 'new world' because its shape resembles a globe. It is a brighter shade of apricot topped with a green leaf. Taste-wise I remain an apricot fan, as the musmala is squidgy with a dry aftertaste.

And so we visit our first stall.

'Merhaba Sedat, Merhaba Baba. How are you both?' we say.

Baba's face lights up. 'Welcome, welcome, come, come.'

'Everything is fresh,' Sedat says. 'Taste the tomatoes, fresh from my garden.'

'Would you like a Turkish or apple tea?' asks Baba.

'Thank you, Baba, perhaps next Sunday,' we reply.

'No problem. We are always here waiting for you.'

And they mean it.

I select what I want from the mountains of fruit and vegetables on display and pay for them.

As I turn to move on, Sedat calls after me.

'Josie wait, a small gift for you.'

He repeats this ritual every week, with gifts of two lemons, a handful of carrots and a small melon.

We say thank you and goodbye, then head off to the next stall where the welcome is similar.

Such kindness. Can you imagine being served tea as you shop in your local market and be given free gifts of food, simply for being loyal customers?

With our produce in cool-boxes in the boot of the car, we stride out along the seafront to The Gocek Brasserie Café. We are more than ready for our breakfast.

Alperen, the owner, runs out to greet us.

'Merhaba Josie, Merhaba CJ, welcome. How are you both?'

'We are well, and hungry, thank you, Alperen. How is your wife, Yengin and little Cemile?'

'They are both healthy and Cemile is growing bigger by the day. I have good news, a big surprise, we have twins coming soon. I am happy, now my job is done,' he says proudly.

We laugh and congratulate him, shaking his hand and kissing him on each cheek.

He guides us to our table and we order his café's traditional Turkish breakfast, the best meal of every day. The fresh cheeses, tomatoes and village eggs are served with pride and a flourish. The homemade jams, local honey and bread, hot from the oven, are divine. My only exception to this traditional fare is to drink good quality coffee at that hour instead of Turkish black tea.

It is a long and lingering breakfast where we sit taking in the sea view and people-watch whilst relishing every mouthful of food. Sometimes we read a few pages of a current glossy magazine or have a brief catch-up on what's happening back in the UK via one of the British daily newspapers.

The weekend edition of the Turkish Daily News is a must for me for a good general overview of news in Turkey and around the world. I like to know what is going on culturally in Turkey and try to keep up-to-date with fashion trends.

It is a calm few hours, sometimes catching up with old acquaintances. The occasional woman passes by dressed in cutting-edge tracky, trainers and full makeup as she heads for her morning jog or power walk along the marina front, iPod in place.

Gocek is one of the most popular and famous sailing ports along the Aegean Sea. To-date there are at least five marinas here. I call it 'Sailing City' in season, a whole other world that does not interfere with life on land.

Clunky trolleys are pushed from the local supermarkets, steered with varying degrees of success by boat-crew staff dressed in their whiter than white t-shirts and shorts. Filled with food, alcohol and fuel they resupply either nearby *gulets* (large traditional Turkish pleasure boats) for day hire, or private mega-yachts whose passengers rarely step onto land. They will shortly set sail across the millpond sea to one of the beautiful tranquil islands or beyond.

Around this time of day, some of the boat people from the *gulets*, as opposed to the 'yachties', appear for a hot chocolate, iced coffee or a freshly squeezed orange juice. They sit patiently, eyes darting to and from the person who is already reading an English tabloid, ready to grab it as soon as they have finished.

In my experience, the boat people live for a minimum of six months of the year on board their smaller sailing boats. When on dry land, they ride everywhere on beaten-up old bicycles and seem possessed of the need to use the internet on a daily basis. By day they loll around in the shade on their boats. By night, there is always a reason to party with their neighbours or anyone who is happy to stay up late and join in the 'craic' and bring lots of booze. They occasionally take their boats out to sail, sometimes heading to a Greek island to buy more booze and the kind of food they loved back in Blighty. Some seem tired and lack enthusiasm and motivation. Maybe it's the been-there-done-it-all syndrome?

The 'yachties' on the other hand, for whom sailing is a passionate seasonal hobby, arrive for perhaps a long weekend or a week. They rent from a local yachting agency purely to sail along the beautiful coastline of southwestern Turkey.

They are identifiable by their loud voices, wraparound Ray Bans, Tag Heuer watches, yellow sailing jackets and leather moccasin boat shoes.

They too like to party and burn the candle into the small hours. However, their commitment is such that they can still get up at the crack of dawn if needs must for a heavy day or days of sailing.

They appear at The Gocek Brasserie Café in large groups, with one starting the order of a full English and coffee. This is followed by a chorus of voices announcing they will have the same, with one additional mutter of 'hair of the dog.'

They eat in silence and soon a voice pipes up.

'Fit everyone?'

There is a consensus of reply.

'OK, let's grab the bill and sail to the islands.'

Will they remember Gocek? I hope so.

Around noon our calm and peaceful surroundings can sometimes be disturbed. Turkish men and their families appear, ready to eat a brunchy breakfast. The men are unshaven, pale and looking grumpy, wearing what looks like sleep attire (get-out-of-bed Istanbulian chic).

With armfuls of the Turkish Sunday papers they plonk themselves heavily into a chair in the shade. They light up a large cigar, and when the waiter appears, grunt, 'Turkish coffee, medium sweet.'

They spend the next few hours reading - or pretending to - lost in their own little world while ignoring the chaos of family life that surrounds them.

Some of the wives are dressed as if ready to walk onto the red carpet on Oscar Night minus their tiaras, eating tiny morsels of food, whilst issuing a stream of orders to the poor nannies. Meanwhile, Mummy's little darlings crash around on their bikes, generally disturbing the silence and upsetting the dogs who move away to get some peace.

Eventually the children settle and tuck into their breakfast, sipping large fruit smoothies and demolishing plates of bread, cheese and honey.

Turkey's 'Loves Young Dream' are the last to arrive at the café. Trendy and beautiful, they find a sunny spot, the guy besotted with the drop dead gorgeous girl sitting opposite him. She is long-haired and tanned with the normal model attributes. Large shades cover half of her face with diamonds shimmering on beautifully manicured hands that delicately hold a long cigarette. She wears a semi-sheer kaftan, slit at the side to show off her long legs that almost hide a skimpy white bikini. They order a traditional breakfast and a Turkish omelette, whilst their eyes remain locked onto each other, the food just a distraction. They eat a little, feed each other, and sit holding hands, kissing and cuddling oblivious to the world drifting by.

At around one, at least in season, the tourist pleasure gulets start to appear across the bay, bringing with them the holidaymakers from Fethiye or further. They stand apart from the locals, as many of the men are clad in vests or football shirts, or simply wear nothing on top. They are weighed down with gold bracelets, chains around their necks, and tattoos stretched across their beer-laden bodies. Many of the older women wear nothing more than a bikini or a cropped top with everything spilling out in all the wrong places. Some would say not a pretty sight and not respectful to this culture. A real contrast to how the traditional men and women dress.

One such lunchtime, I happened to be in the market about to purchase a kaftan for the beach, when to my right I heard loud banter with a stallholder.

'Hiya, all right mate? Luverly jubberly,' said a male voice booming like foreigners do. 'Mine's a size forty-six mate, got that, a forty-six?'

I turned to see a larger-than-life man with a stomach to match. He had long thin grey hair, knee-length white shorts and a red football vest festooned with a long 'statement' medallion.

His wife and another couple were gathered around the shoe stall to join in.

The husband carried on. 'Yeah, them ones over there, mate. No, them, look, they are white. How much?'

The stallholder replies, 'For you, only fifty lira.'

'Blimey, fifty lira,' the man says, making signs with his hands to the poor vendor, letting him know that the price was too expensive. 'I'll be back later mate to try them on. Keep them out for me, yep think I fancy white. All right mate?'

He gives the poor Turkish man a thumbs-up and heads off giggling at what he thinks is humour for his entourage, clearly never intending to come back.

After such shenanigans and many purchases, some of these holiday groups return to the town centre to wander along the quiet main street, or fill the restaurants on the marina front to enjoy plates of chips with tomato sauce, downed with a few beers or glasses of white wine, followed by ice cream.

By four in the afternoon the tourists board their gulets for the return journey back to their holiday by the beach.

Everyone breathes a sigh of relief as peace and calm returns once again to our little sailing port. Like a mother hen to her chicks, we are territorial and protective of this oasis of tranquillity that we have come to know and love.

Tales from Turkey

Tales from Turkey

The Bearer of Bad News

My Housekeeper is a clever lady,

She cooks, she cleans and sews.

She washes like a thing gone crazy,

But then she shrinks my clothes.

My silk, my cashmere are no more,

My curtains no longer tip the floor.

I show her how, I show her why,

As she smiles, 'OK', and still I cry.

Without a whisper or a word,

Things get burnt or shrunk unheard.

Some clothes are twisted, some are torn,

My wardrobe now looks so forlorn.

So with each wash day

I'm no longer precious about my clothes.

Our friend Yusef, visited us from Ankara.

Over a cup of morning coffee, he happened to mention a golden nugget of information. He informed me that the Turks do not, traditionally, like to be the bearer of bad news. They either ask a friend or even a friend of a friend to pass on any bad or sad news, or simply say nothing until eventually, as time passes, you find out for yourself.

At Pink Pines I am beginning to understand how this custom works.

Selma arrives one morning and works for an hour. Appearing from the kitchen she announces 'Josie, I cannot stay. I need the remainder of the day off.'

Why does she tell me one hour before she is due to leave?

In fairness, she prepared breakfast and made the bed before disappearing.

A few days later I'm getting ready to head to the beach to swim. I ask Selma where she put my new bikini bottom she washed last week?

'Oh,' she replies, head down. 'That went in the rubbish.'

'Why?' I ask.

'It got burnt when I was ironing it.'

So basically she ironed the arse - apologies for the Irish colourfulness - out of my new leopard-print bikini bottom and did not mention this fact in case I might be upset. As I had only worn it twice, yes, you could say I was upset. The iron was obviously far too hot. I didn't ask her to iron them, since when does swimwear need ironing! I am not known to have diva tendencies, and life is too damned short to iron swimwear.

On returning from Blighty, I find silk and cashmere jumpers shrunk to fit a six-month old baby. They are as hard as Plaster of Paris, stuffed into drawers, never to be worn again. Did anyone care to mention these laundry mishaps? Of course not.

In my absence, new silk and cotton curtains were washed and shrunk. Not on my instruction, normally I take them to the professional launderette. Selma re-hung these pieces of fabric at half-mast in the lounge and bedroom as if I would not notice. And my husband's comment? 'Well, at least they still cover the window frame.'

So these last few years, armed with a little more knowledge, I have developed special radar with eyes in the back of my head.

One hot sunny morning, sitting on the lower terrace having brunch with CJ and my parents-in-law, I spied some bad news in the distance. There on the clothes line were two peculiar-looking shirts that looked 70's hippie-style tie-dyed. On closer inspection, I discovered that Selma had put one of my shocking-pink pashminas in with two pale-coloured linen shirts on a forty-degree white wash. I bought the shirts for CJ's birthday and he had worn them once.

Luckily, Mum-in-law, Lady J, was on hand to advise. She took them back to the UK, and using a special soap the colour was eventually restored to said shirts. Would Selma have mentioned this? Oh no, they would have been carefully hung back in the wardrobe until CJ needed to wear them, or perhaps not.

More surprises were in store when I opened the glass cupboard to find two heavy thirty-five year-old hand-blown Waterford crystal wine goblets with big chips knocked out of them. I find another special glass, resting upside down in a top cupboard away from harm minding its own business, with the stem snapped off.

Does anyone inform me of these breakages? Of course not.

Nobody knows how or why these accidents happen in our house.

Ironically our large container, shipped over from the UK with many of my worldly goods, including a delicate dinner service, my glassware, large glass vases and kitchen equipment, ner a thing was scratched or broken, with one exception. I un-wrapped one sturdy glass vase to find it cracked straight down the middle. The cracked vase, as it happened, marked the end of a long Irish friendship, so that was okay.

On another occasion, returning from Blighty, I discover the telephone does not work, the washing machine is leaking water and the dishwasher will not run its cycle. Oh, and we have a snake's nest in the collapsed carport roof. To top that, I discover that a mouse has been living in the bonnet of my car all through the winter months and has chewed the cable that connects with the ignition. So that's why the car would not start. Finally, to my great sadness, twelve bright-pink bougainvillea flowering bushes which have been growing for over five years, have all died over the winter season too.

Why?

Well a certain 'plant devil' forgot to put them in the sheltered area as I had suggested before our frosty cold winter appeared. Yet when I telephoned every two weeks from Blighty, I was constantly assured, 'Everything is good.'

I probe gently and ask Selma questions. In response, I get a shrug of her shoulders or her hands are thrown up to the sky as if to say, 'It was those demons up there, they did it' or 'I don't know, it just happened.'

Away from the domestic challenges, bad news might be a worker not showing up to paint the outside of your house. Why? Well, he was called away at the last minute to do another job, even though you had booked him months ago.

One day I drove forty-five kilometres to have my hair cut. I entered the salon and asked for Murat, with whom I made the appointment. Blank expressions greeted me from the staff as they shrugged their shoulders, pointed me to a new salon recruit and carried on working on their client's hair.

I booked my appointment a few weeks prior with Murat, and I confirmed with the owner of the Salon, Birgul, the day before. She had assured me that it was 'no problem'.

So here I am, ready and waiting, with no sign of my hairdresser or anybody wishing to explain, when I hear a Turkish person use the phrase.

'It's no problem.'

Alarm bells go off.

After many questions, Birgul appeared. 'Murat is not here. No problem, please take a seat. This man will cut your hair,' she said, pointing and then giving instructions to a young boy.

'Are you saying my brilliant hairdresser has left? Why could you not tell me on the phone?'

Silly me, stupid question. Birgul looks away, upset and disappointed. It was my turn to leave.

A good hairdresser is right up there next to our best friend. So when he or she moves salons without a word and we are expected to put ourselves at the mercy of a total unknown, it is indeed a major tragedy, yes even worse than losing that best friend.

In our supermarket, I find the meat counter. 'Do you have any hindi (turkey) today?'

'It's coming,' the butcher replies.

'When?'

'Come back on Friday.'

And so I do, only to find that there is still no *hindi*. When I ask again I am told, 'It won't be delivered until next Wednesday.'

The ever-smiling assistant takes my telephone number again. He confirms he will let me know when the *hindi* is delivered.

This game can go on for weeks. So in the end, you give up. There is no sign of the damned turkey. You never get the call and it never comes.

Then one day you happen to be food shopping in the same supermarket. Like a magnet you are drawn to the meat counter to find packets of the stuff just lying there. Did anybody bother to let you know?

Again, of course not.

The pièce de résistance comes at the start of the hotel tourist season when the head chef tells the owner of the hotel that she is five months pregnant. She already knew she could not cope with working in the extreme heat or be able to work the full six-month season. Did she inform her boss so he could make other arrangements? Of course not.

Good chefs, like good hairdressers, are hard to find and oh so difficult to keep. You can imagine the 'air turning blue' during that conversation between the chef and her boss. Such upset could have been avoided, but that is not the way here.

Back at Pink Pines, the straw that broke the camel's back came when Selma was cleaning my twelve-year-old white Wedgewood teapot. The service was dear to me, a wedding gift from my family. With a flick she bashed the spout on the ceramic kitchen sink, which caused it to break off.

CJ, clever man, used glue for crockery and promptly stuck it back on. Phew, what a relief, it would cost a lot to replace the same pot. All was well for a week when Selma did the same thing.

Again, CJ came to the rescue and glued the spout back in place. But not for long, the same thing happened again only with more elbow strength, so now I have a teapot minus its spout.

This much-loved dinner service has sadly been reduced to being chipped and cracked, all done whilst I am not around, and still never a whisper of the damage done.

Initially, I became upset and angry. I would raise my voice and point my finger, but it has no effect, only on myself. Of course with the passing of time these things make more sense. Not being the bearer and giver of bad news is the Eastern way. It puts another piece of the ever-revealing jigsaw of Turkish life in place.

Since then, I have become philosophical. Breakages and clothes can be replaced, eventually. I would rather focus on the positive things Selma does each day. How would she have any value on my possessions, how would she know what is precious to me? Clothes and crockery are purely a functional matter for her. We come from two opposite spectrums of the world of what is important.

With this knowledge I have come to a big decision. When I replace my china to correct the feng shui in our house, it will certainly not be Wedgewood or any kind of fine bone china. Oh no, I shall invest in the simplest, most durable, bounce-off-the-floors-and-walls Selma-proof crockery. And neither Selma nor I will ever again worry about breakages, nor will she have to be the Bearer of Bad News.

But this tale is not quite finished. As I write, I walk past the washing machine to notice a few white items spinning with some dark-coloured ones. Oh dear, my French cotton and lace tops are being washed on a 40° coloured wash.

And so the damage and shrinking continues. I feel a heated discussion about to take place. Obviously, those little 'red devils' have appeared again and continue to create havoc.

Looking on the bright side, I can pass these clothes on to Selma's children and her family in Mugla. Perhaps this is her way of helping me to de-clutter, whether I want to or not. Or perhaps she wants to encourage me to buy and wear more practical Turkish village-style clothes? No more silk, cotton, linen or cashmere for me. Maybe it's time to become that traditional Turkish lady after all.

Adventures and Shopping in Dalaman

Through forests of green pines, the potholed road to Dalaman is marked with rusty bridges and other hazards, climbing and descending through the mountains like a curved rollercoaster stretching over twenty kilometres. Closer to Dalaman, the terrain flattens and spreads out to replace the pines with the colours of lemon, orange and grapefruit trees lining the route. Sadly, the cotton fields have disappeared and in their place pomegranate bushes with their crimson flowers are growing strong. Pomegranate is the new fruit in this area and exported in vast quantities. Of course, Western marketeers would have us believe it's the new miracle health food, packed with vitamins.

We arrive, shaken but not stirred, in this typical Turkish working town. Like most, it's showing signs of change, with more modern apartments and houses being built both in the centre and towards the hills to accommodate Turks from the larger cities. The English, Dutch and Germans also wish to live here. Development in the area is thankfully a slow process, like watching an olive plant bloom, growing strong and yielding fruit some years down the line.

In Dalaman, there are quirky shops, mostly used by the locals, that meet my needs for the house and garden. There are traditional cafés, some with glass fronts and others with dark interiors with wood lining the floors and walls. Here the Turkish teapot takes pride of place on a gas stove along with the pot for making proper Turkish coffee, the smell wafting in my direction. The locals love to sit, commenting on the daily news whilst reading their morning Turkish papers. I enjoy being amongst them, people-watching as I sip my morning black tea too.

There is a new café-bar on one of the now 'safe-to-walk' side streets were a green plastic rug is used to give the illusion of grass to cover over the dips and holes in the pavement. Walk through it at your peril and don't wear high shoes.

Quality 'Illy' coffee is served here. They need some barista training to make a perfect strong Americano, but I am impressed and grateful to drink a decent coffee.

Today is Thursday, a buzzy market day where the farmers and villagers from the other smaller local towns descend upon Dalaman. First they head to queue in one of the packed banks on the main street. Tractors, bikes and some antique beaten-up cars push to find a parking space.

Then it's time for us to walk away from the main thoroughfare, through narrow, uneven, soon-to-be-called 'streets', to the market where families carry bags ready to be filled with fresh produce and vegetable planting for the garden.

The market is a mishmash of stalls that also sell grains, pulses, household bits and pieces and basic *kilim* rugs made from either cotton, wool or even plastic. Clothes of every sort and colour are displayed for babies, children, men and women. Even that 'certain type' of ladies underwear can be bought here. In one corner there is a fish shop selling varieties of farmed and sea fish.

On the adjacent dusty unfinished streets there are traditional restaurants with bright-orange tables and chairs outside. Some of the best kitchen food is served here with chiller cabinets displaying fresh *mezes*, and on either side, small cubes of meat on skewers called *şiş*, are ready for cooking.

The ever-familiar Co-Operative Tea Shop is on most street corners where men of a certain age and position meet to sit in the shade to play backgammon and catch up on the local gossip whilst drinking copious amounts of Turkish tea throughout the day.

Walking back through yet another narrow street, I enjoy viewing some old stone houses where men and women of older years sit outside, surrounded by metal containers filled with flowers and aromatic herbs of basil, thyme and sage. They unhurriedly peel and chop their vegetables for lunch and evening meal oblivious to me, the foreigner, passing by.

I pass the main mosque and feel the calm atmosphere. Friday is a holy day in the Muslim religion and only men from the villages and towns wearing their best shirts, suits and caps head to the mosque for prayer. The men wash their feet and hands from taps in the wall and drink from the water fountain above before they enter the building. After sermons and prayers, outside is again a time of social interaction with friends and acquaintances. It reminds me of times past in Kinsale, where on a holy Sunday the local farmers would gather, be last into the church to stand at the back, and first out to have that much-needed woodbine after the service.

Back on the main street, crowded deli-type shops serving Dalaman and neighbouring towns for many years, serve cheeses, thick creamy yogurt, dried fruits, Turkish delight, and *helva* that tastes like a combination of nougat and sugar. The Turks love all things sweet. There are big bowls of giant green and black olives, yellow village butter, eggs and local flower or pine honey. Vats of *tahini* to make hummus, or mixed with grape syrup and spread on bread for breakfast, are set out in a display cabinet.

There are bread shops that bake *simits* (a traditional bread ring covered in sesame seeds) and a brioche-style bread called *açma*. Squares of corn and light rye are also sold in small batches.

One family-run bakery on the corner of the main street is particularly enticing; the smell of the bread, and friendliness of the owners draws me in. I keep my guard as the baker removes another thirty loaves from the hot clay oven using a long wooden pole that could poke a customer's eye out. I'm here early and the bread is still warm. Sold with a smile and a cheery bid for a 'good day', I leave with my fragrant baked treasures and look for my car for the journey home.

Back in our village, Selma's sewing machine is at the ready; making clothes for her children, husband, family and neighbours? I have an idea. Perhaps it's time she made a traditional summer skirt for herself. I want to treat her, so I ask her if she would like to join me on my next morning excursion to Dalaman. After much cajoling, she shyly confirms the following Thursday market day to come shopping to buy the fabric. This is a first for us to head out together to the 'big smoke'.

The week passes and I collect Selma at the bottom of our track. Dressed in her best black trousers, head scarf of sky-blue and white flowers edged with fresh cloves with their perfume wafting in the car, we are ready to head off. I ask her to choose a CD and she carefully checks through my collection and choses 'Love my Breath' by Destiny's Child. We bumble along the windy road, sun roof open with it playing in the background.

Thirty minutes later we arrive in Dalaman, and I park the car in the shade of a back street.

I turn to Selma.

'How about going to my favourite tea shop and bakery for Turkish tea and cake first?'

She nods and says, 'Okey'.

As we step through the door, the smell of cinnamon fills the air. Freshly baked Turkish cakes, decorated with swirls of cream, fresh fruit with red, shocking pink and blue coloured icing, are on display to tempt us. I smile and note a photocopied sign stuck with black tape to the front door advertising:

'Healthy Meal'
Freshly Squeezed Orange Juice and Cake
Healthy Protein

Hmmm, I don't think so. We order tea and share a sweet tahini bread. We make our way to a table and Selma asks the waiter for some unchilled water for me. She is so sweet, so thoughtful.

To my left sits a smartly dressed, intense-looking Turkish man, reading his paper. He gives the odd glance in our direction over his dark-rimmed glasses. He becomes more interested as we sit and sip our tea with our occasional exchanges in Turkish. I can sense he wants to strike up a conversation. In a matter of moments he leans towards us.

'Would you like to come to my house and sample some of my homemade wine? I can sell you a few hundred litres, no problem. Indeed, do you have any friends who would like to do the same? I could come to your home and we could have a wine party.'

He waits for my response. I simply smile.

'I am recently retired as headmaster at the local school,' he continues, 'and have taken up winemaking as a hobby. My wife is still working, my days are spent alone. I have two sons at university in one of the big cities and I am lonely. I know many European people here and can make introductions to help you make new friends in Dalaman.'

Such an enthusiastic spiel is unexpected.

Without drawing breath he asks the usual questions, 'Where are you from? Are you married? Is your husband Turkish? How long have you lived here? What do you do? Where do you live? Do you own your own house? How much did you pay for it?'

It is far too early in the morning to be quizzed in this way and by a stranger with verbal diarrhoea.

'I have a rule,' I say. 'I never discuss money or age and I enjoy being quiet in the mornings.'

Not in any way put off, this ex-headmaster turns to Selma and proceeds to give her the third degree in Turkish, not realising I understand every word. 'Who is this lady?' What is it like working with her?' he pushes her for answers.

Oh please, enough. Give me a break. I feel that we were both being harassed and our space invaded.

The calm Selma is tuned in and keeps her voice low and responses vague.

'J, it is time to go,' she says.

Post-haste, we politely pay our bill, bid our farewells to Sebil the owner and make a swift exit back onto the hot main street.

'J, that man asked far too many questions. He thought he could make money out of you. I could see he was causing you big stress.'

She takes my arm and we walk down the street in the glaring sunshine.

'Selma, thank you for your words of wisdom, you knew exactly what that man was about. Now let's go find fabric for your skirt.'

After that unexpected distraction, we head in search of the hidden fabric shop. It is a mystery as to where it might be. Selma asks every other woman along the way. They shrug and say they do not know of one. Then out of nowhere we spot a haberdashery, tailors and shoe repair shop on the other side of the street. The outside windows, one on either side of the entrance, are a pick and mix display of what they sell: children's shoes, toys, men's underwear, men's shoes and shirts. The biggest display of all is devoted to racy lingerie in red and black, modelled on odd-looking female dummies for all passers-by to view. And there in the corner, leaning against one of the windows are a few faded rolls of fabric. I have seen this material as skirts and pyjama-like bottoms on many of my elder Turkish neighbours dating back some thirty years. Stuck to the door is a hand-drawn red arrow in felt tip pen directing us to the back of the dimly-lit shop.

In the subdued light, a woman is working on her sewing machine, surrounded by more rolls of floral fabric. Perhaps this trip has not been in vain.

Within seconds of stepping inside the front door there is a flurry, like vultures descending on their potential prey. We are surrounded by an entire family of women and men of all ages forming a circle around us, staring and talking in excited high-pitched voices at the same time.

I smile, acknowledging them with the usual pleasantries.

'I am looking for skirt fabric that must be a natural cotton or linen in this summer heat,' I ask. 'What colours do you have?'

The twittering entourage follow me as I walk around the back of the shop. I pull out the odd roll of fabric in between the family appearing with lots more which are unsuitable for my lovely Selma. I ask Selma for her opinion. She bows her head. Of course the family who own the shop are inquisitive as to who I, the foreigner, am and ask why I am with this young traditional lady?

The air and atmosphere is stifling. Feeling hot and bothered, I realise we stepped from one situation into another more intense one. I feel I am in a witches' cavern filled with cackling voices.

Looking across at Selma I see that she is not enjoying being in this crowded space either. I also do not realise at the time, that it is her first outing with somebody alone who is not a family member since moving to the village some twelve years before.

With irritated impatience and a wish to leave, I choose a plain rich blue fabric that feels like a mix of linen and cotton, and will do the job. I call again to Selma and hold the fabric up for her to make a decision. Again she wants me to choose and merely says, 'Okey.'

'Let's pay and get out of here,' I say.

Relieved, Selma nods and we escape with the family calling after us, 'We are here and waiting for your return.'

The following day, Selma reveals that, like me, she does not enjoy crowded places, too much chatter and intrusive traffic sounds. How brave of her to venture out with me and our lucky escape.

Once recovered from her Dalaman ordeal, Selma appears one morning in her newly designed skirt. It is a wraparound-style with some well-placed fasteners all the way down the side to meet her sandals. She has made a belt in the same fabric tied up in a big bow at her waist.

She looks like a 'whirling dervish', flowing and twirling. A vision as flashes of her olive skin and long jet-black hair contrast with the bright blue of the fabric.

She looks beautiful and content as she glides through her day in her new skirt. That said, I have not seen it since.

'Why do you not wear your skirt?' I ask.

'I am keeping it for good wear and the next family wedding,' she tells me.

Three years have passed and still no sign of the skirt. I hope it is hanging up and out of moths harm in a safe place for that next special day.

Many months later, after a check-up at my dentist's surgery in Dalaman, CJ and I step into the same bakery for a restoring Turkish tea. Who should be sitting in the same seat holding court with three foreigners as his audience? Only the retired headmaster turned 'winemaker *par excellence*' giving the same spin and spiel to his latest audience. They hang on his every word.

Those Poor souls…

Tales from Turkey

New Dentist in Town

Thanks to our Istanbulian friend we registered with a new dentist whose practice is the most up-to-date south of Istanbul. His name is Tarkan after a famous Turkish singer (think of a young Donny Osmond in the musical 'Joseph'). Thankfully, he does not sing while working inside your mouth.

Tarkan set up his dental hospital in Dalaman two years ago. I could never have imagined receiving such friendliness and hospitality at 'Dalaman Dent' as it is called. You see, life in Turkey, even in a dental surgery, is at a different pace and speed from the West. Whatever the treatment involved, it takes as long as needed, no hurrying or clock-watching here. Tarkan even takes the bookings himself. With my first appointment confirmed, he gave me precise directions to the main street and location of his practice in Dalaman. Mind you, I still couldn't find it without help.

On a sunny September morning, I drove to meet him for what I believed would be a quick check and clean up. I arrived early, knowing I would have to ask for directions. Maps and directions are 'a man thing', or so men would have us believe. In my case it's true. I headed to the bakery for help. Sibel the friendly owner looked puzzled.

'J, I have not heard of this new dentist. Please sit, have a Turkish tea and I will check with my friend the jeweller. He knows what is happening in Dalaman.'

She leaves and the tea arrives.

I see the jeweller come out of his shop, then run along the pavement to another shop with an insurance sign above it two doors down. A tall man who did not look Turkish - no thick black moustache - appeared and recognised Sibel. They came into the bakery and took a seat opposite me.

'Merhaba, nice to meet you, I am Tolga. What language would you like your directions in? I speak French, English, German or Turkish,' he said, proudly.

'Oh, let's try French today, just for the hell of it,' I replied. 'Once upon a time it was my second language.'

Animated with many hand gestures, he gave directions. 'It is a hundred meters from here on the other side of the road. There is a big sign over the entrance. You can't miss it.'

You want to bet, I thought.

I finished my tea, shook Tolga's and Sibel's hand and thanked them both for their help. I crossed the road and arrived at the fruit and vegetable shop to be told the dentist doctor is next door.

And there it was with a bold sign over the entrance: 'Dalaman Dent'. How could I have missed this four-storey modern building in the centre of Dalaman with long windows of smoked glass and a giant Turkish flag hanging from one? A colourful logo displayed a giant tooth wearing sunglasses lying on its side on a beach under a palm tree with the words 'Dis Hekimi' (Tooth Doctor).

I entered the building, noticing the lift straight-ahead which will take me to the third floor. I decided to climb the stairs for a little exercise and to gather my thoughts. I arrived a little huffy and puffy into what I can only describe as a Hollywood set for VIP's.

Large open double-doors opened in to stylish reception rooms with soft leather sofas that could swallow you up. Purple velvet-covered chaise longues allowed you to stretch out while you waited for the call to the surgery. Full-length floor-to-ceiling windows stretched across the room with panoramic views to the hills and Dalaman Airport.

A uniformed dental nurse appears.

'Ah, you must be Josie Maguire, we have been expecting you. Would you like tea, coffee or a fruit juice while you wait for Mr. Tarkan?'

I ask for a glass of water, which she serves on an embellished traditional metal tray. The calm setting and hospitality blows me away, I feel I am in a six-star hotel. For a moment I forget I am here to see a dentist in a small town in southwestern Turkey.

Ten minutes later, I get the call to the surgery. It's a pristine room, minimalist with mirrors, chrome cupboards and green glass worktops. In the centre of the room is a peach reclining chair. On the wall is a large framed photo of Marilyn Monroe blowing kisses from a blinding, whiter-than-white, set of teeth. In front of me are floor-to-ceiling windows.

'Good morning, Ms Josie, you find us at last?'

My new dentist's handshake is strong. He is a small, balding man, his face and eyes kind and caring. Between my average Turkish and Tarkan's few words in English, I know it will be okay.

With great ceremony they helped me onto the chair into an almost prostrate position.

'What music would you like to listen to?' Tarkan asked.

Well, that one threw me.

'Music?' I said blankly.

'What about some Ser-ahhh Britman (Sarah Brightman)?'

'Oh, yes please,' I replied.

I relaxed, listening to her album 'Eden'.

Tarkan started procedures by checking my teeth with the dental nurse at his side, her pen poised writing descriptions of each tooth and his instructions on a flip chart in front of me. I gazed at the undulating mountains and natural landscape as he infiltrated my mouth with various metal devices.

'Stand up, please,' Tarkan asked.

He led me to an X-ray machine to photograph the troublesome teeth. The results appeared straight onto a computer screen. We discussed the results and agreed the work that needed immediate attention.

Injections, I now love them. I know, strange woman. The needles are so fine, I don't feel a thing when they enter my gum. I could have these injections every day, as I feel good for a few hours afterwards without a hint of pain when it wears off.

I am lost in 'Eden' with a numb mouth, my eyes closed. My dream is broken with what I believe is Tarken's favourite phrase.

'Spit please.'

Just as I have had enough, hey presto, all work stops in my mouth. I am helped off the peach recliner and guided up another set of stairs to a sheltered roof terrace where Tarkan's wife, Suna, welcomes me. She is pretty (think of a young Kim Novak), dressed in sparkly-white pedal pushers, with an equally ornate kaftan and matching bejewelled shoes. Her nails are painted and she wears dazzling diamond jewellery.

Her assistant prepares to serve Turkish tea, coffee and water. I relax on a large wicker chair and listen to the sound of the birds, watching the occasional plane land at Dalaman Airport.

Visiting my dentist is a time for unwinding and feeling pampered.

The following week, Tarkan sent me a text saying that my bridge had arrived and can I come immediately.

I text him that my car is being serviced.

He offered his car, and his son Faruk as driver, and to be ready in forty minutes. Forty minutes later there is the honk of a car horn outside Pink Pines. I made my way down the marble stairs, with the dogs throwing a barking wobbly.

I was impressed by being chauffeured in a metallic-blue, convertible Mercedes. The sun was beating down with temperatures of over thirty-two degrees, but inside it was air-con and luxury all the way to Dalaman.

Once the bridge was fitted, Faruk was ready to take me home again. How many dentists do you know who would instruct their son to do a round trip of seventy kilometres?

On the way back Faruk put the soft top down and suggested the scenic route home. We overlooked the sea, and with the sun shining on my face, a scarf around my neck and my hair blowing in the light salty wind 'The Ballad of Lucy Jordan' by Marianne Faithfull, came to mind (also the theme song in the film 'Thelma and Louise'):

'At the age of thirty-seven, she realised, she would never ride through Paris in a sports car with the warm wind in her hair…'

I was being driven through Dalaman doing just that, high on injections and not a care in the world.

What an experience it has been these last months at 'Dalaman Dent', made all the easier because of this man's care, skill and professionalism. He is a true craftsman. You name it and he can do it with teeth. With more than thirty years of experience of working in Turkey and Germany, I believe he is a miracle worker in dentistry.

In fact, I look forward to making further appointments to have my front teeth crowned top and bottom. Perhaps, in the fullness of time, I too shall be blowing kisses from a large photo looking like Marilyn Monroe, so watch this space and the local advertising boards as you drive to and from Dalaman.

'No Buns in Turkey'

The bunting is out and the champagne is flowing. After three years of waiting, it is time to celebrate. Finally, I have a live internet connection at Pink Pines. As I sit and write each morning, I enjoy listening to BBC Radio 2, especially the humorous Ken Bruce and his sidekick Lynne Bowles. Their banter and chat across the airwaves puts a smile on my face.

One morning, Ken got a bit carried away as he introduced the next record.

'Come on Kylie, show us your Buns.'

He was talking about the elfin Kylie Minogue and her derriere. I laughed out loud. It was quite unexpected, especially at that time of the day. Little did I know that a week later a different set of 'buns' would be on full display at my traditional Turkish beach.

Visiting the beach is 'me' time, where for a few hours, I relax and recharge. I enjoy swimming way out to sea, performing my style of water aerobics in relative privacy. Back on dry land I stretch out on my sunbed, shaded by a fragile and floppy umbrella, whilst listening to the healing sound of the waves. No intrusion or interruption.

One hot, summer morning, that all changed. A middle-aged man of rotund shape appeared with his wife on the beach. His skin was bright pink, having spent many hours in the sun. His body was glossy as if smothered in baby oil. He proceeded to lie on his front and pull down his clingy black Speedos to expose a rather large white bottom.

I was emerging from the water at the time - Ursula Andress-style, or so I wish - and yes I stared at this sight in disbelief. Shocked? No. Surprised? Yes. It was not a pretty sight for a gal so early in the day, nor would I wish to inflict this view on anyone at any time or season.

Gentlemen, ladies, can somebody explain to me why men of a certain age and silhouette seem to have an attachment to what they perhaps wore in their youth, and feel the need to wear skin-tight Speedos with little left to the imagination? Is it in the name of a tan, or are they going through a midlife crisis? Have they looked in a well-lit, full-length mirror lately?

Oblivious to their onlookers, the couple pulled out a bottle of local white wine from a chiller pack and drank from plastic cups, all the while laughing with big guffaws of noise. Soon they ran into the sea, plastic cups still in hand, frolicking and shouting 'Wheee…', splashing each other like a pair of young kids. Suddenly, the man tripped on a hidden rock - opps - and fell over, spilling his precious wine and losing his plastic cup. It bobbed up and down heading out to the horizon, gone forever. They went quiet, and with that little drama over, returned to their sun loungers. After observing the antics of these two having fun in their special way, I returned to enjoy the view of the crystal clear blue waters thinking that perhaps I was the one missing out.

At midday, I headed to the co-operative beach café, a makeshift wooden building with a service hatch. Overhead, bamboo slats acted as shade from the direct sunlight. There I ordered my usual water and Turkish tea from one of the teenagers who work at the beach during the summer months.

By this time, the couple were sitting on the corner of the terraced area, holding hands and drinking large beers whilst facing directly into the searingly hot sun. His Speedos were pulled down as far as they could respectably go - well, more or less - to get his front bits tanned.

His wife was wearing a t-shirt with a plunging neckline.

'Ah this is the life,' she said as they clinked their glasses, kissed each other full on the lips and chuckled simultaneously.

A few Turkish women, camped at the beach for the summer with their families, sat in a circle at a table nearby, knitting. Their eyes occasionally strayed to the two foreigners. Perhaps they wondered what it might be like to have some of that 'loved up' feeling after so many years of marriage to the same man, or they wondered what it would feel like to wear so little clothes without inhibition.

At this same beach there is also a friendly, curly-headed blonde man from Germany. He is tall of stature with a slim tanned, muscular frame. He lives in a mobile home for at least four months of each year. I have christened him Adonis. He too has a leaning towards Speedos, his being navy blue with go-faster silver stripes down the sides, accompanied by a blindingly white toothy smile to contrast with his dark tan.

Draped around his neck is a thick chunky gold neck piece. A further gold jewellery display and large statement medallion, adorns the rest of his torso. He greets me with a big 'Hi' and a wave, his layered bleached highlights shining brightly in the sun. He delights in speaking the same few words in English each time we meet, ending with a weather update.

Throughout the morning he happily struts his stuff up and down the beach, moving back and forth across the café.

At some point he has a cold shower from a nearby rusty overhanging pipe before sitting in the café sipping Turkish tea. He chats with the locals who accept his attire and macho-man look. Later - to attract further attention - he climbs onto the roof of his mobile home to adjust his satellite dish or redirect the awning that hangs above the door.

Maybe there is a secret Speedo club set up for men around the world for those who cannot let go of that feeling of Lycra next to their bodies? It's probably best for me not to know.

After another beach visit a few days later, I was packing the car to leave when a small, moustached, thickly-set man stopped me. His car was parked right beside mine.

'I have seen you on the beach many times, are you French?'

I was flattered, 'No, I am Irish. French is my second language.' I was about to prepare my response in French when this stranger went into full flow and gave me chapter and verse on his background.

'I am Turkish. I live in Paris during the winter months. I have a summer house near this beach and I have a big apartment in Istanbul. Ah yes, I also have a son who works in London.'

I must have sounded interested with my exclamations of 'mais oui', 'mais *non*', '*v*raiment' and 'alors'.

'You speak excellent French,' he said, even though I hadn't had the chance to say very much.

I smiled, thanked him in Turkish and said I must head back home now. I opened my car door, got in and started the engine, only for this man to walk forward, lean in and put his face and cigar fully in the frame of my car window. My attention and eyes were drawn to his black teeth.

'Would you like to join me for dinner this evening? We can drink wine, converse in French and gaze at the stars in the clear night sky.'

The song I heard myself silently singing was 'Voulez vous couchez avec moi ce soir (would you like to sleep with me tonight)?'

What a proposal. Err, no thank you, not on your nelly.

'I really don't think so,' I said. 'My husband is waiting for me at home and would not be happy for me to meet a strange man for dinner.'

His face retracted from the window and his expression in any language was something to see. The look of disbelief at my refusal of his 'one night, one night only' offer perhaps hurt his pride, or was it a Turkish manly arrogance? Whatever, the conversation came to an abrupt end. He waved me on and walked away chewing on his unlit cigar. I could hear the words of my Irish grandmother in my head: 'I am sure he was very respectable, what with owning all that property.'

As flattered as I was to be told I looked and spoke excellent French, that day I was happy to drive home to my husband and his pearly-white, clean teeth, fresh breath and Colgate 'Ring of confidence…' Zing...

The following Sunday at Gocek market, standing at Sedat's fruit and vegetable stall, I noticed the same man walking in my direction with his mother, a traditionally dressed wife and three young children. I wondered about his beach proposition. Had he been 'chancing his arm' as the Irish saying goes? Did he visit the beach on his own in the hope of meeting a European woman who might one day accept his 'romantic' offer of sitting under the stars?

I pulled my hat down to meet my shades, and slipped away into the day.

A few weeks later, it was one of the last days of the season when the man who runs the beach café appeared at my side.

He insisted on carrying my drinks on a tray to my sunbed with a plastic side table. Although a first, I did not think anything of it. I accepted his offer and thanked him.

He smiled his toothless, red-faced smile.

'The sun is very strong today. I can put sun cream on you and give you a massage all over your body? I am always here to assist you in any way.'

There was an unmistakable leer.

Oh really? I thought. Here we go again.

'My husband has already put sun cream on me and will be joining me shortly,' I lied.

With a scowl he turned on his heels and headed back to his chair in the shade of the overhead bamboo by the café. He remained there for the rest of the morning and ignored me. I was much relieved.

Under the same bamboo shade, the other teenage boys working at the beach, play backgammon, as is their wont each day. They only come to life when the girls arrive in their finery to pose on the beach each afternoon. These testosterone-fuelled teenagers nudged each other, giggling and laughing at my expense and at 'Romeo' who runs the café.

So ladies, the moral of the story is, listen and learn these lessons for Turkey: don't flirt, make eye-contact, speak or give the local Turkish men any encouragement, especially when at the beach. I speak from experience and I am currently looking for a different beach for next season.

In the words of Greta Garbo, 'I vant to be alone.'

Tales from Turkey

Tales from Turkey

You better Watch Out

Y ou may have your traffic congestion and road challenges where you live, but we have our own set of car challenges when driving or walking up and down our mountain road from Gocek to Pink Pines.

Once out of the port, driving off the main road becomes a rough 'off-piste' track more suited to quad bikers than cars or bikes. If you are looking for that adrenalin rush then this is the place for you.

It appears to have slipped the minds of the local mayor and councillors that the road needs repairing after the rainy season. The road is covered in mud, sludge, sometimes huge boulders, or branches from trees that fall onto the road. The soil crumbles as the water falls straight off the mountain and gushes down the road moving everything in its wake. What was a road yesterday is a river after the rain.

During the summer months, when the temperature rises to over thirty-eight degrees, the road becomes a dust bowl. In parts we have on-going tar lifting off the surface, which resembles a sticky mess like thick treacle.

On other occasions, you bumble along full of the joys of the day when suddenly around the corner is an old rusty truck moving at a snail's pace carrying giant stones from a quarry some thirty kilometres away. Heavy trucks create large potholes and craters, causing havoc for the car's suspension and our nerves. Like the crest of a breaking wave we rise and fall as we drive. Mind that pothole and don't fall into that crater! Jolt, thud, bang – too late, you just did.

There are other obstacles too. I've ended up stuck behind a tractor with the family sitting up front. The trailer attached is filled with bales of hay, red bricks and a large dirty bull. The trailer sweeps gently from side to side as it makes its way to the bottom of the narrow road.

I 'beep beep' and flash my lights at the driver who ignores me for a few kilometres and then suddenly drives into the grassy verge to finally let me overtake with a big wave and a smile from all.

On another day, my journey was slowed by a car full of sheep keeping Grandma company as she sat in the back seat. With a large basket of vegetables and greenery on her lap, she beat off the sheep as they tried to push their faces into the foliage. I did not want to think of the smell coming from that particular vehicle.

Whilst walking early one morning, we came upon an elderly couple in their eighties. The husband was sitting in the middle of the road with a pickaxe, chipping away. His intention was to place a long piece of water piping across the road to enable them to have free mountain water from the streams that abound us.

His wife was wisely sitting at the side of the road, her clothes tucked into her pyjama-type bottoms half way up her leg. She was tending to a traditional tea-maker on top of a small gas stove. I happen to know that they are both deaf and do not talk a lot. They were completely oblivious to the occasional noise of any oncoming cars.

'Merhaba günaydin' (hello, good morning'), we said as they looked up to greet us with smiling faces. As we carried on walking, we waved down a few cars which were being driven far too fast. We explained to the drivers that there was an elderly man sitting in the middle of the road on a dangerous corner by the village graveyard and to approach the corner with caution.

What a relief to bump into this couple on our return home and see them still alive and happily going about their normal job of caring and tending the wild garden and flowers where their dead are buried.

We smile each time we pass this graveyard. There is a bus shelter with a water fountain to the left of the main green gate. Quite often, propped up against the wall of the bus shelter are two wooden coffins. The deceased arrive on the back of a truck wrapped in a white sheet, and are transferred to these makeshift coffins for relocation to their final resting place. This is reality and the simplicity of life here in the village. You come into this life with nothing and you leave pretty much the same way.

One afternoon as I rounded onto the mountain track heading for home, I was quite startled. There in front of me were a herd of sheep and goats with thick brown and black shaggy coats blocking my path. I noticed a strange figure to my left. 'What an odd place for a statue,' I thought. It moved a few minutes later and turned out to be the shepherdess. On her back was a large sack and a few branches, she was crouching down with her leg cocked to one side as if in terrible pain. Not so, she was going to the loo with her wraparound hessian skirt hoisted up around her middle. Without underwear or care for decency, everything was there to view.

Her face was craggy - 'well-lived' you might say - and her arms long and sinewy. I could see the back of her hands were gnarled from years of cutting down branches and bushes to feed her flock. She had a thick piece of rope wrapped around her waist that obviously was used to tie up some of the animals. Most likely her life was spent on these mountains in all kinds of weather conditions. The wild outdoors her home and bathroom.

Within minutes, her skirts were pulled down and life resumed as she directed her flock to the other side of the road and back into the forest. Then she turned and walked over to the car and mumbled something to me with a mouth full of gums. All I could make out was, 'gel, gel' (come, come). I reached over to my bag and took out a bottle of water along with a fresh *simits* and passed them to her. Her face lit up as if she was just given gold dust. She mumbled again, 'thank you, thank you, have a good day.'

'My pleasure,' I replied. 'Eat well.'

My path was now clear to drive through.

Ah, special moments.

Warm late spring sunshine seems to affect everyone, especially our tortoises. It is not uncommon to come across a pair who decide to mate in the middle of the road with no consideration for the right time or place. Other times mummy and daddy tortoises are out in force, teaching the babies the codes of the mountain roads.

'Now off you go kids, cross the road and keep your head in your shell when you hear a noise.

Keep walking straight ahead and don't stop until you feel the soft green beyond the road, under your feet again. We will stay on this side until we know you are safe. Nod your heads when you get to the other side.'

'Now if a kind driver comes up behind you, let them pick you up and carry you to the other side, no hissing or peeing or any other funny business. They are only trying to help you.'

This is the good advice that all protective tortoise parents give to their young ones.

The tortoises have been known to cause traffic jams as they stop for a rest halfway across the road. Most drivers get out of their vehicles, pick up the tortoise with the rear end facing away from them, and set them down on the other side of the road. Then everyone can get on with their day. I have to admire the tortoise's bravery, as once they are in the middle of the road there is no going back.

At night, we have the added excitement of hares with rather long legs running sporadically across the road. They look like baby kangaroos, and I am not hallucinating or hitting the Raki bottle. It keeps us on our toes and gives us something else to watch out for along this route.

The Highway Code for village driving can be a little confusing. Examples of local 'road signs' include:

A ball: could mean a large hole in the road, but could just have been left by a child.

A moth-eaten hat or an upturned Fanta bottle stuck on a stick in the middle of the road: could mean another hole in the road, even deeper than the sign with the ball. Or 'men at work', probably sorting out a burst water pipe, which is a regular occurrence. The workmen are probably sitting nearby in the shade having one of many Turkish Teas.

A t-shirt placed over a large branch: could mean boys play football here, so slow down.

A sheep's skull perched on a few large rocks one of top of the other like a pyramid in the middle of the road: at night it could mean, beware of yet another hole or crater in the road. No flashing lights or triangular signs here, just a glimmer from the empty holes where said sheep's eyes once were.

The perfect sign you need in the pitch dark... bump, crash, wallop... oh dear, I think we have just hit another pothole.

And three well-placed dirty nappies in front of a car means: 'The car has broken down and awaiting assistance, silly.'

After two years, finally someone must have heard our little prayer. For as if by magic one afternoon, two large and ancient pieces of machinery, probably the nearest thing to trucks, tipped their load of a mixture of clay, sand and pebbles - smelling very strongly of seaweed - onto our driveway. Martha barked herself into a frenzy at the invasion.

Ahmet, Selma's husband, walked up our dirt track with a large rake and shovel in his hand and smoothed over the dumped material.

At last we are the receivers of, shall we say, some of the ground-covering material we were waiting for. Half the job is done. Hurrah, we have a slightly smoother surface on which to park Charlie, my angel of a car, under the car port.

Since this delivery, I am on neighbourhood watch waiting to hear the sound of another ancient truck heading towards Pink Pines to finish what was started. Bricks are needed before the rainy season washes all that clay, sand and pebbles away.

So far there is neither sight nor sound of such a vehicle coming in our direction. I have asked my neighbours. All I get is a 'don't know' or 'soon'.

I remain hopeful that in the fullness of time our dirt track will be completed, and be as smooth as silk - well, shot silk with some rough edges - and that will be a job well done at last.

Tales from Turkey

The Puppy Tale
(Not tail)

One chilly November morning, CJ stood on our top terrace looking towards the bendy road through the pines trees. He spotted a puppy looking enthusiastically in his direction. The next day, out walking, the puppy appeared again. CJ waved at her. Well you do, don't you? On the third morning we found the puppy in the chicken shack taking shelter from the cold wind.

This fluffy puppy meant the chickens no harm, although you can imagine their horror as they tried to lay their morning eggs. She was just hungry and in need of cuddles.

Where this puppy came from, who knows?

Set into her small face adorned with white and tan markings, flanked by pert tan-coloured ears, were her adoring brown eyes. There was definite border collie from the neck down. She had an upright black-and-white feather boa-style tail and a precise walk with a female wiggle. We had never seen a dog of this breed in the village before.

Did CJ and I need another mouth to feed, especially a puppy? That said, all my feelings turned maternal.

I voiced my concerns to CJ about what to do with a puppy in terms of injections and health check-ups. How would we train and feed this little mite? Most importantly, the ten-thousand Turkish lira question, how would Martha react to her?

No problem, Husband came to the rescue. Thankfully, my dearest CJ is like a magnet to dogs, they seem to sniff him out. CJ and gentle Martha have shown me how to enjoy their company and unconditional love without fear.

Despite this, we spoke to one of the ladies who runs the local official dog sanctuary about rehousing her. The sanctuary was full. She asked if we would agree to foster the puppy for a few weeks while a new home was found for her. That seemed fair to us.

So we christened her Selina after a Turkish friend of ours who has piercing dark eyes too (was she flattered? I don't think so).

By now, Martha was sleeping by our fireplace in her cosy sofa bed each night and ate her dinner in the kitchen. She was a less anxious and happier dog than in her challenging years of survival prior to adopting us. She had a routine she was thriving on, so Selina's arrival initially had an unsettling effect on our Martha. Perhaps Martha thought her position as 'top dog' was about to be overturned by this whippersnapper from nowhere? She was not about to accept any dog stepping onto her patch, even as an overnight guest, never mind a female puppy living with us. She set the boundaries on that first morning so Selina knew who was boss. Three short, sharp barks did the job.

'Listen kid, I'm in charge here. I have lived with these guys for a while and have a nice life, and no dog is going to take that away from me. This is my space, okay? Accept that you are here on my terms and we will get along just fine. Got it?'

Martha settled back into her bed, exhausted after her assertive speech.

Selina's response was to wander away, tail between her legs, to a patch of sun where she curled up and closed her eyes.

We bought her a small scrunchy sofa bed to match Martha's, along with another feeding bowl. We placed her bed in our marble-floored utility room and office under the house.

After a month we decided that keeping these two apart at night was crazy. It was time for them to sort themselves out and bond or not. So one night, with a little trepidation, we put them both in the office, gave them their food at the same time and walked away. Later we reappeared to see how they were doing. Well, what a surprise, all was calm, each in their beds doing their pre-sleep ablutions. With sighs of relief we bade them a goodnight and headed back up the stairs.

Thankfully, peace has reigned below stairs ever since that night.

As time went by, Martha became more maternal towards Selina. Occasionally she gave her three warning barks to back off and behave if she got up too close and personal. Sniffing Martha's bum is a definite no-no.

Then one day a miracle occurred. Early one morning, as they were let out of the office, Selina was overheard to say to Martha.

'Come on Mart, let's play.'

'I am Martha to you, if you don't mind. A little respect here please. Anyway, how do I play, that's puppy stuff isn't it?'

'Look, just copy what I do,' Selina said as she launched herself at Martha.

Stunned, Martha stepped back and barked. Selina, growing in confidence by the minute, was not easily put off and launched herself again. This time Martha ducked and sidestepped, turning around to face the pup for the next attack which quickly came.

It was soon apparent to Martha that the only option was to literally throw herself into this new activity. She realised that the missile-like Selina, was going to use every trick and opportunity at her disposal to attack in the name of play.

Selina had acknowledged from day one, 'I'm a puppy, this is what I do; run and play all day if I can. Just walking every morning is for wimps.'

Poor Martha did not know what she had let herself in for.

As the weeks passed she got the hang of it and subjected Selina to a little of her own medicine. She pinned her to the ground first thing in the morning. That's my Girl, we agreed. You have got to remember that Martha is Labrador size, so Selina had to duck out of the way pretty quickly if she wanted to avoid being stunned by this heavy force lunging at her.

There is no doubt that Martha has become Selina's stepmother. They are now 'the terrible twosome', little and large as they wander the village on a daily basis. No squirrel, cat or neighbouring dog, male or female, is allowed across our threshold without a fight or chase and a lot of barking. Perish the thought that a stranger or a car might appear on our dirt track without these two warning us and telling them they are not welcome until we have acknowledged they are friends.

The man who comes to read the meters for our electricity is larger than life. He dons an Army General-type hat and rides an old rusty motorbike. The dogs do not like him, his hat or the noise of his bike. So he is frightened and can only walk up our drive chaperoned by Selma, even though the dogs are all bark and no bite.

Selina and the chickens happily move around each other even when she tries to eat their food. Martha is disgusted that these three are buddies. Ahmet has created yet another double water trough out of wood. There is now a queue each morning as George the gecko, along with Mattie and Beatrice, like to drink from the same container as the dogs. I even spotted our two newly-arrived love doves having a few sips in unison.

Sometimes Martha and Selina give each other little kisses, so sweet to watch. Like Martha, I have learned patience and gentleness with a firm hand, whilst training Selina. I always praise her when she responds to a command. Praising Selina comes naturally to me much to the chagrin of my husband, who feels he does not get enough praise himself even when he does what he is told (some of the time).

To see this puppy happy and developing into an affectionate companion has made our job worthwhile. Animals are a wonderful example to us humans, every day they wake up full of the joys of spring, happy and hopeful that the day ahead will bring them all they need. They are trusting and loyal, wanting to be loved and fed and given lots of attention and affection. If we are honest, isn't that what makes our world go around and give us that feelgood factor too?

This 'puppy tale' has a happy ending for now. Martha has gained a playful loyal buddy and inherited a stepdaughter. She has learned how to relive all that she missed out on as a puppy, yes playtime and the fun that it brings. She is more confident, has a new sleeker and toned body, and is now the most respected elder spinster dog in this village.

As for Selina, well she has found a great friend, mother figure and protector in Martha. We know she is grateful.

We inherited two anxious and nervous dogs, perhaps these are the characteristics of strays. The sound of gunshots as the villagers hunt wild boar before dawn puts the wind up both of them. At the sound of lightning or thunder, they hide under the table on the top terrace or bark to be let into the safcty of the office downstairs where they curl up under my desk.

We live in hope of them overcoming their demons and fears in the fullness of their doggy life as we have learned to do as humans.

And five months later? We remain the sole owners and guardians of this fireball of energy. We have decided to keep Selina and go on this puppy adventure, all of us together.

Tales from Turkey

Carpet Cleaning in the Mountains

When Selma removes anything resembling a rug, carpet runner or any kind of floor or wall covering from our house, I know summer is here. Over a few days each one will be washed lovingly by hand.

Handmade woven Turkish carpets have been an integral part of Turkish history and culture even before nomadic times. The word *kilim* refers to the way a carpet is made. Kilims are not just rugs, they have a multitude of uses as tents, luggage and floor spreads for guests to sit on. They are even hung as coverings for doorways and walls to keep the cold draughty winds of winter at bay.

Silk wall hangings and pillowslips were made for the many opulent palaces in Istanbul and Europe many centuries ago. These handwoven rugs continue to be used as mats for praying or eating from, and even used as storage bags to this day. Now I know why traditionally Turks take off their shoes before entering a house or special buildings, so no dust or dirt enters from outside.

In the twelfth century Marco Polo was so enchanted by the wool and silk fabric used to weave such vibrant-coloured kilims that he wrote about them, and so spread the word about these creative art pieces across Europe.

Of course it was women who learnt the craft and skill of weaving with special motifs and symbols for each area. History tells us it was their way of expressing their thoughts and dreams. My Turkish history friend tells me that secret love messages and terms of endearment were designed by these women as they worked them into the carpets for their lovers.

At Pink Pines, there are no 'secret love messages', just rugs made with simple materials of either goat's hair or sheep's wool with cotton backings.

I remember the first summer Selma announced it was time to roll up the carpets and runners.

'Why' I asked.

'It is becoming too hot and dusty to have coverings on these floors. You do not want to find ants or other insects setting up home in your carpets as the temperatures rise. I must wash and clean them. Then prepare them for storage for the next few months.'

She assured me that it was a fail-proof system used since she was a little girl on the family farm where she watched and helped her mother and grandmother do the same at the beginning of the hot season.

I went along with her knowledge of such things with no idea of what she was planning to do. In the UK, I would simply telephone the carpet cleaning company and make an appointment for them to come and steam clean the wall-to-wall carpets and rugs in the house. The operation would take a day to clean the carpets and a few days to dry out. With steamed up windows, the use of chemicals and a lot of money exchanging hands, I was never convinced that my carpets were any cleaner or smelt any fresher.

With my approval, Selma set about the task in hand.

Instructions by Selma for summer cleaning of carpets at Pink Pines

First, ensure the house owners are in the middle of eating a calm and peaceful breakfast on the upper terrace when carpets and rugs start to fly over their heads. This makes for an additional kick-start to their day.

Carpets are thrown over the balcony, beaten with a stick or baton and then flung onto the terrace below. As they hit the ground with a bang, Martha, our elder dog, panics and runs for cover on the lower terrace. Selina has already taken refuge under the breakfast table.

Brush around and under the area where the carpets have landed. Then place them flat on the clean ground.

Fill a large basin with warm water, add lots of liquid natural olive soap and sprinkle onto the carpets.

Turn on the outside cold-water tap and hose down carpets until they are soaking wet (note both Martha and Selina become even more nervous realising they are likely to be next on the washing list).

Slip out of your shoes, roll up your trousers to well above your calves, and start some light on-the-spot jogging up and down on the carpets.

'Selma what are you doing?' I ask, mesmerised. It looks like she is crushing grapes.

'I am making sure the fabric soaks up all the water,' she smiles.

Once the carpets have absorbed the water, it's time to get down and dirty on your hands and knees. With a large soft scrubbing brush, scrub gently the soap and water mixture together using long strokes up and down the fabric and then across the weave. This requires patience, time and energy (it is important to be at a reasonable level of fitness and agility for this cleaning procedure).

Hose down the carpets with more cold water until soapy water is cleared and terrace is spotless.

(The dogs are still hiding).

Roll up each piece of carpet or rug inside out. Place standing up on one end in the sun to allow water to drain off. As this will take about thirty minutes it's time to relax in the shade enjoying a Turkish tea or coffee.

Once recharged, unfold the carpets and hang them over the balcony, giving the appearance of a carpet bazaar shop display. Allow the rest of the day for them to dry.

The following day, brush all the carpets and roll up the floor coverings to store in a cool dry cupboard or room until the winter months appear again.

Rescue Selina and Martha from their respective hideouts, hose and soap them down until their coats are shiny and clean. Let both dogs have a treat of some tasty biscuits while they dry naturally in the shade of an olive tree with drinking water at their disposal.

(Later we brush and groom them with love).

Follow the above instructions and you too can have gleaming clean, dust free carpets, rugs and dogs. With no use of chemicals or machinery, this effective old-fashioned way works, done for a cost of around five Turkish lira.

Note - do check weather conditions before attempting.

I have heard carpet traders in Istanbul tell their potential buyers to 'build a relationship' with their carpets, as they already have a life history passed down from one ancestor to another over hundreds of years. How? By suggesting that the buyer hand-washes their purchase once or twice a year themselves so they get to know every weave and knot of the fabric.

So this is your 'opportunity' to do the same and build a better, eco-friendly, greener environment. Try this at home wherever you are. Why not surprise and influence your neighbours? Show them how it's done. You may even make a new friend from right under your feet.

One more tip, a tried and tested method on how to store your 'shaggy pile rugs' during the summer heat:

Place your shaggy rug on the ground, first ensuring it has been brushed and vacuumed. Place a handful of cedar shavings, or cotton wool doused in cedar oil, in the centre of the rug and fold in half.

Then repeat as point two and fold the rug again.

(Time for a five-minute break with a cool glass of water, remembering the high temperatures).

Now the really challenging part (ask for assistance from a husband, a family member or a neighbour is a good thing). Roll up the rug, then ask assistant to help put it in a large recyclable plastic bag and tie with a piece of natural string.

Store in a *kabin* (spelt with a 'k' in Turkish, i.e. an outhouse or shed) for the entire summer.

(It's time to have yet another deserving long cool drink in the shade, after a job well done).

Five months down the line, the carpets will be in perfect condition, with your shaggy pile rugs smelling of fresh pine air, with not an insect or hole in sight. Cost? Roughly three and-a-half Turkish lira.

The only fly in this environmentally-friendly ointment is that Selma remains convinced that chemical mothballs do a better job.

'Josie, they are the only repellent that works every time,' she insists.

Not swayed by her view, I continue to use the natural product of cedar oil or cedar cubes. I have seen the damage these destructive village moths do to natural fabrics and wool. They have mouths like razor-sharp drills that go through several jumpers at a time creating perfect round holes. CJ can confirm such desecration to his much-loved knitwear. He considers his clothes and jumpers as good friends, so it took much reassuring that we could restore his knitwear to being wearable again.

Lucky for CJ, Selma came to the rescue with her resourcefulness. With her finest embroidery needle, she embroidered some well-placed manly red and green flowers to cover up these holes.

To date, I am grateful that the village moths have side-stepped my carpets and woollens and I can report that they remain intact and protected at Pink Pines for now.

Tales from Turkey

Ah, it's Saturday

Don't you just love that Friday evening feeling, the weekend stretching out ahead of you? Two days of total relaxation to do whatever takes your fancy. Pure bliss.

Even though CJ and I live at an easy pace in tranquil surroundings, we value and look forward to our weekends. They are sacred times for us to recharge and have two peaceful days together.

Saturdays generally flow smoothly with the exception of last weekend. At eight in the morning, the sound of beating drums woke me gently. They are a sign that a local wedding is about to take place.

Ah the drums, the drums. They resonate strongly with me. They are part of the deep-rooted culture of Turkey, and indeed Ireland where we have the bodhran played in small country pubs or hotels at many local functions. In Turkey, the drums are a whole other story, with many different types and shapes of handmade varieties from all parts of the country. They are covered in either a goat or sheep skin on both sides to give a different pitch or sound.

In this village the drums beat out for one to two days while the wedding is celebrated.

Back to my neighbours wedding when, the day before, the future bride and her cousin surprised me by arriving at ours on an old beaten-up bike to deliver a wedding invite.

Wedding celebrations can vary from village to village according to the families' standing in the community. Here, there is no such thing as two years of planning in advance and spending thousands of pounds on designing the wedding stationery and the wedding reception. However, money is spent on the bride as she is the centre of attention.

The bride's wedding dress makes a bit of a statement. Traditionally, it is white and can sparkle with shimmering crystals. It is always teamed with a red sash or belt, as part of eastern tradition. Waxed, manicured, pedicured, hair coiffured and styled - because she is worth it   the bride will be looking the best she will ever look. From the tips of her toes to the top of her head, a bride is a picture perfect 'princess' on her special day.

This particular invite was a simply typed card with the name of the bride and groom, the family names, and where the celebrations were to take place over two days. The invite was attached to a roll of newspaper tied up with a piece of lilac ribbon. On opening the newspaper a white and lilac towel dropped out. Why the present? I still have no idea but what a lovely thought. I thanked the bride and wished her good luck in her preparations.

I went to the kitchen, made myself a cup of tea and propped myself back up in bed to ponder my day ahead. I was awake during the night and so I was feeling a little dopey and slow. CJ was lost in Izmir some four hours away, so the day was mine, or so I thought.

I took a shower. As I came out of the bathroom while towel drying my hair, I became aware of a loud sound close to the house. Heavy drilling? Scratching? Vibrating? Could it be a pending earthquake? No, the metal toilet roll holder did not jangle.

What the hell was that noise? I marched across the lounge and looked out of the front window. Crikey, a bright yellow JCB digger was working on our driveway, lifting great chunks of red soil and dirty great big stones out of the rock face just below the house. Heaven forbid that we would be given prior notice or warning. The noise was deafening.

I realised that finally the area for our cars was being dug out to enable us to drive down the dirt track out onto the narrow main road.

I phoned CJ.

'Oh yes, the man was due to come last week,' he said, far too cheerfully. 'Sorry darling, I forgot to mention it to you. That's Turkey.'

We were told that here in the mountains you have to be grateful when workers turn up. I felt anything but grateful at that precise moment.

Hungry, yes.

When Selma arrived, she had henna on her hands, which is also a sign that a wedding is about to take place nearby. She prepared my breakfast, laid it on a tray and carried it outside to the sunny top terrace. With the pounding noise resounding around me, it was impossible to eat. Tray in hand, I walked back into the kitchen and re-laid the table with food. I tried to eat calmly with earplugs in place, but with the floors vibrating it was a bit of a challenge.

With breakfast over and earplugs removed, I could hear men in loud voices underneath our lounge windows. Again I moved to the top terrace, outside the front door, to view what was going on. I could hear the sound of someone mixing and scraping some kind of fluid around in a container. Below me were Ahmet, and his old friend Volkan who lives some thirty-five kilometres away, mixing water and white paint in a big plastic bucket and proceeding to slap it onto the wall under the staircase (a sort of whitewash emulsion paint). They were in deep discussion on the work in hand.

I ran down the stairs like a madwoman.

'Volkan, what are you doing? Please move all the plants and garden furniture out of the way and wash the walls before putting on this … this white stuff. Who told you to do this work anyway?'

My voice and anger was rising. Again CJ did not mention anything about painting the outside prior to his departure to Izmir.

Volkan put his hands up to his face and looked the other way, which made me even more agitated.

'Speak to Selma, speak with her,' he said in muffled tones behind his hand. 'I cannot speak to you.'

Oh for heaven's sake, what's his problem? I thought.

'I will not be treated so disrespectfully nor have I any wish to "Talk to the Hand".'

I took a few deep breaths, stormed back up the marble stairs into the house to find Selma.

'What is going on here?' I asked. 'Why are the men painting under the stairs? Why can the job not be done properly, like moving the plants and furniture away from the wall, then washing down the wall and using real paint? And why is Volkan covering his face and not replying to my questions?'

Selma calmly took my hand and guided me to the kitchen.

'Josie, please sit down, let me make you a Turkish tea. I will explain why Volkan is talking to you in this way.'

Once the tea was made and poured, Selma sat with me.

'Volkan is only doing what is perfectly normal and natural in our culture. Please do not get angry with him, he was simply trying to help Ahmet. CJ said that the outside of the house was in need of a paint. They wanted to surprise him for his return.'

What about a discussion or a plan first? Not here.

Selma continued in calming tones. 'In our culture, especially in these small villages, a man cannot talk or look at another man's wife. It is disrespectful.'

Eventually I did calm down and rationalised yet again how different our cultures are. Here I was, this feisty Irish woman who was used to running businesses for many years, instructing men and women, getting things done and never giving it a single thought. Volkan, poor man, must have been a little taken aback by my forceful and rude outburst. How was he to know how to behave towards this hysterical foreign woman? Equally, how daft of me to get so worked up about them painting a wall that wasn't how I wished, or even knew it needed to be done?

To my relief, Ahmet and Volkan only whitewashed a triangle of wall under the marble stairs, so I chose not to say anymore on the matter.

They left for the day, leaving a trail of white blobs all over the terrace and drips of the watery white stuff on the plants, wooden garden chairs and table. Guess who would have to clean it up? Women's work, don't you know.

Finally, after four hours of constant intrusive noise, the metal monster and its driver left the area too. Oh joy, silence was the best gift I could have received that morning. Peace was restored.

Later, feeling a little more energized and more peaceful, I took a long walk up the mountain, breathing in deeply, that clean fresh healing air. Once I reached the top, I stopped to admire the stunning views sweeping down across the valley and mountain towards the traditional Turkish beach of Inlice Bay. On my way back down the mountain, I passed the house of the bride where many hands -

women of course - were busy preparing for the evening's wedding party. White plastic tables and chairs were being unloaded from a trailer attached to a tractor. A few men in open dirty shirts half-heartedly worked on placing an awning overhead in between sturdy trees.

The smell of cooking saturated the air as the women lit large open fires, placing steaming cooking pots, the size of oil drums, on top. An older craggy-faced man bent over a large dry, grassy patch with a scythe in his shaky hand, slowly hacking away the overgrown area. The chairs and tables would be lined up on the hopefully more even ground later. As with all Turkish village weddings - they are no small affairs - the elders must have pride of place with a good view of the bride.

Surrounded by cables leading to large speakers, was a teenager testing the sound system. Other male family members were standing on rickety handmade ladders and chairs, putting up some makeshift lighting that would illuminate the traditional musicians who would arrive a little later, adding more atmosphere to the proceedings after dark.

Amongst all this activity, the first three of the official musicians appeared with a wish to practice once the sound system was in place. Live Turkish music evokes great emotions and feelings. It is wonderful to dance to, especially for those whose feet and hands are less coordinated.

As I walked up the dirt track to my house, I spotted Selma, looking very hot and bothered. Opposite our new car area, she was digging furiously with a large pickaxe. She suddenly grabbed a spade, throwing massive amounts of red soil over her shoulder. She looked up, wiping the perspiration from her brow and face with her headscarf that was originally tied around her head like a Bandana.

'Josee, I am very unhappy. The digger man dumped rocks and soil on my young fig trees. I have to save the fruit.'

She looked exhausted. You have heard of digging for buried treasure, well this was a case of digging for buried fig trees, 'gold' to the villagers, as every fig is precious.

The ever-dedicated Ebru, Ahmet's mother, is in charge of organising the stall to sell the local produce at the market, inclusive of fresh figs in season. It is similar to a co-operative. The unsold fresh figs are eventually dried in the sun on Ebru's steps that lead up to the back of her unfinished house. Once dried, they are weighed out on a scale kept on her terrace. There she sits on a cushion, legs stretched out in front of her for hours at a time. She dusts the figs lightly in flour then puts them through string to make a circle, half a kilo at a time. They will be sold in Gocek's Sunday market some nine kilometres away.

The drums continued their gentle beat as local villagers, family and friends began to arrive, the high pitch of excited voices and laughter filling the air with wedding anticipation. The rising smoke increased as even more fires were lit.

No such thing as buying a new outfit for this reception, just show up as you are and you will be given a thousand welcomes. The guests here are not competing to wear the most expensive designer outfit or the latest 'must have' bag, shoes or accessories.

This is simplicity at its best, letting the bride and groom be in the spotlight on their day. The bride will have been whisked away by the female members of the family early that morning to the beauty parlour. Then it is time for her to have her fantasy photo taken with her groom, either before the ceremony or the day after. This photo will be framed and admired forever.

My head buzzing with all the sound, it was time for me to head to rest and sleep for a couple of hours, again earplugs firmly in place.

It was nearly dark when I awoke to the sound of music and flashing lights. The chatter and banter of the guests, along with animated children's laughter resounded around and down the valley. The wedding party was in full swing. The walls of my house were thumping.

I stood on the upper balcony to take in the ambience and excitement of the evening. The smell and smoke of meat being cooked on a barbecue wafted upwards and towards the house (perhaps a goat or sheep had been killed for this special occasion). I could not see a thing but the atmosphere was electric.

Below me, on our lower terrace, lights were switched on. There in the yellowy shadows, head down, arms outstretched in the traditional male pose, and clearly oblivious to anyone, was CJ, dancing as only he can - the left foot does not know what the right foot is doing - to the live traditional Turkish group. No longer lost in Izmir, but lost to the sound of the music.

He looked up.

'Hello darling, I thought I would surprise you. How about a romantic dinner under the stars tonight?' I smiled as I went into the house to open a bottle of white wine from the fridge. I grabbed two glasses and returned to join him. We stood on the lower terrace and raised our glasses to each other. The happy wanderer had returned. Then we turned to toast the bride and groom in the misty smoky distance.

I lit some candles and hung some oil lanterns on the olive trees around us. We enjoyed a dinner for two soaking up the heady atmosphere that surrounded us from the wedding party. Later, as we retired for the evening, all was well again, my Saturday was complete. The drums carried on 'a-beating' and the live music played until eleven o'clock sharp (as the law rules here), lulling us into a relaxed and deep slumber.

I never saw the bride in her finery, nor did I ever meet the groom or see either of them again. But I wish them good fortune, a long and happy life together made complete with healthy children. I am sure the 'wedding photo' is in pride of place in their home for many years to come.

Tales from Turkey

Epilogue

Three years on and I continue to survive. Living this changed life up my mountain retreat, a walk in the park it is not. But what an education and journey I continue to experience. This Irish woman is integrating into village life and has been accepted by her dear Turkish neighbours with all her foibles and funny Western ways.

What have I learned? Well I set out to find a way of managing my health. But the path I have walked has led to so much more. I view the world in a different light where material things and grand gestures are no longer high on my list. There are many ways of doing, being and living.

What matters to me?

I value health, love and good friendships and the calm relaxing environment. It continues to inspire me.

I am grateful to have been led to this village. No need to hurry, no need to rush, things get sorted and resolved when they are meant to.

My passion for Turkey and learning about this eastern culture grows and deepens.

CJ continues to love a local wedding where he can dance for hours with his Turkish friends without rhythm, still working with his two left feet and nobody cares.

I hope you enjoyed reading Josie's fun adventures.

Although this first book has come to an end, the stories continue to evolve.

Watch out for updates and news of the next in the series *More Tales from Turkey* which is already a work-in-progress. Thank you all.

For details, got to the website:
www.talesfromturkey.com

Tales from Turkey

Acknowledgements

I owe huge gratitude to where I live in southwestern Turkey.

Thank you to Richard Tredennick-Titchen who met CJ on a flight from Istanbul to Dalaman. He suggested that CJ drive to the village I now call my second home. It was the first thread to weaving the magic carpet to my new life.

I thank my loving Turkish family for their continuing inspiration to live simply and peacefully.

Writing the book was the easy bit, the 'I' in this project. However, the last year would not have come to fruition without the special people I mention below. No writer is an island, so once you decide to publish, the 'I' becomes 'we'. There are a team of people who I am forever grateful to.

To Chris Gee who interpreted my initial simple ideas on setting up the first incarnation of the *Tales from Turkey* website, thank you.

Thank you to my dad for his love of language and languages. And to my mum, sisters and all my family for their kind supportive words and good wishes, especially on the last leg of getting the book to publishing.

To my dearest friends who continue to will me on, and who encouraged me by telling me the stories were great, even in their raw state at the beginning of this journey.

To Ashley and Sarah Lawrence of ABC Networks at Maidstone who I was introduced to in January 2013. If ever proof was needed in how relationships are built then look no further. And thank you to the members of ABC Networks for your friendship and help.

To Pete Bresser as we sang and laughed in the rain on the morning we shot the photo for the inside of the book jacket. It's a wrap. Thank you.

Social media works! In April of 2013, I first listened to Channel Radio, Kent on Tuesdays, to Jules Serkin's Scoff and Quaff show followed by The Business Bunker Show presented by Paul Andrews with again the magnetic Jules co-presenting.

Two brilliant shows of what is happening in and around the Southeast and Kent areas on supporting local food producers and local businesses. Again, building successful biz relationships. In between Turkish power cuts, signal failures and a dog who does not really want to hold an aerial, we connected via twitter and built up a relationship over the airwaves from up this mountain.

Fast-forward to August 27th 2013. I was invited by Paul Andrews to be a guest on the Business Bunker show to talk about *Tales from Turkey*. What an honour.

To Jules and Paul who guided me on the day and who continue to support me, a massive thanks guys.

To Tym Lawrence for his brilliant and creative illustrations for each story. You have brought them to life. He immediately tuned in to how I wished them to be. I love them. Thank you.

To Tim and the Think Tank Inc team for their incredible insight into what sells and what appeals. You wisely threw my ideas out the window and created a book cover that is so 'out there' and appeals to my new readers. I love the result.

Thank you to Miles Allen, my editor and publisher at REDBAK, who understood my vision and saw the potential during the initial brainstorming for the book. Your knowledge and advice walking me through the last year has made the project so much easier. We have learned a lot together.

To my sister and dear friend Ursula whose unconditional support helped me with collating and indenting the original stories for *Tales from Turkey*. You bought reams of coloured paper to send the material out to agents, publishers and editors. Please send me the IOU. A big thank you.

To CJ, my husband and Superhero. You continued to believe in me, even when I lost faith and confidence in what I was writing. For your patience, the incredible work you have done quietly behind the scenes and your great love, I owe you an extra big thank you.

Finally, to my dear followers across the social media and readers, thank you for taking the time to read my blog for the last year and now my first book of short stories, *Tales from Turkey*.

Tales from Turkey

Interview with Miriam McGuirk - 2013

Q. *Changing from a successful career, especially such a high-energy one, must have taken tremendous courage. Was writing something you felt compelled to do, or was it something you wandered into?*

A. I fell into writing full-time by default. It happened because of life-changing circumstances. My first unpaid writing project was over thirty years ago. I met with an editor of an Irish broadsheet paper who asked me to write some articles and to do some interviews. It was a challenge but I completed the articles as requested. He asked me to consider working full-time for the paper. I declined his offer. It had no meaning back then, it was just fun to do. Now I feel compelled to write every day. It's part of who I am and part of my daily life.

Q. *And how easily did writing come to you?*

A. Twelve years ago, I started writing poetry and loved the fact that it flowed so easily. I enjoyed the process and was able to complete each poem in two days. That gave me the confidence to expand and develop my writing. We Irish are famous for our storytelling. There was a story to tell. It's been easy, like having a conversation with a good friend.

Q. *So Tales from Turkey is your first book. Why that idea, and were there any others in contention at the start?*

A. At the start of my writing journey, my intention was to write Irish Catholic and Guilty, a story of growing up in the Sixties and Seventies in Ireland. The books are sitting on a disc as a work-in-progress.

Turkish culture and the way of life is different to how I live in the West. That grabbed my attention and interest.

Once I moved to my mountain retreat, I began to learn the language. That allowed me to integrate into village life. Inspired by the environment, it gave me the impetus to write of my adventures and experiences.

So Tales from Turkey was born.

Q. *I understand it's based on real events and characters. Does that provide any difficulties in having enough good material?*

A. Tales from Turkey is based on my real experiences and adventures with real characters over the last ten years. I continue to be a keen people watcher and observer of daily events that take place here, still alien to the West.

The material and ideas continue to fill my notebooks and my laptop, there is no lack. Every time I walk up the mountain or down the valley or go to the Turkish main towns, I continue to be inspired.

Q. *I presume you're still spending time there and life goes on. Is there going to be 'More Tales from Turkey'?*

A. Yes, two more books in this series of short stories are planned and a wish to publish my Tales from Turkey blog with details to follow.

Q. *And for those reading this, who is a typical person who would like your book?*

A. Tales from Turkey is an escape from everyday western life, an easy read with my stamp of Irish humour and sense of fun. In the frenetic, buzzy, bizzy world of Western society with everyone seemingly time-short, I believe this book has a significant place for the reader. Any armchair traveller, any reader who has visited the real Turkey and for any reader who enjoys learning about a new culture, this book of short stories is for you.

Q. *Are you publishing in both languages and countries?*

A. The plan is to initially publish in the UK and Ireland. Then to follow with other English-speaking countries and then publish in Turkish.

Q. *So if somebody decided they wanted to write a book, where would they start?*

A. Start writing every day. Join a professional writing workshop as recommended for your type of writing.

Q*. And what's your top piece of advice for somebody thinking of changing careers to become a writer?*

A. If you are financially secure, by all means give up the day job. Otherwise stick with a secure salary and write each day. Do not stop until the book is finished. Then seek out a good and recommended editor, then find an independent publisher or chance your luck with the traditional publishing route.

Tales from Turkey